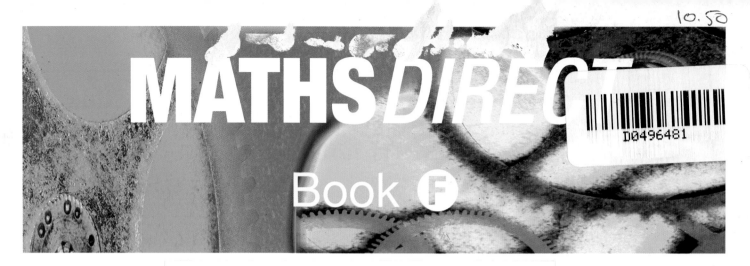

MATHS DIRECT

Book F

This item has to be renewed or returned on or before
the last date below

TWO WEEK LOAN

004582

Collins Educational
An imprint of HarperCollins*Publishers*

Contents

Published by Collins Educational
An imprint of HarperCollinsPublishers Ltd
77-85 Fulham Palace Road
London W6 8JB

The HarperCollins website address is www.fireandwater.com
© HarperCollinsPublishers Ltd 1999
First published 1999
ISBN 0 00 322495 3

Mundher Adhami, Jean Cheshire, Christine Collins, Mark Pepper and
Anne White assert the moral right to be identified as the authors of this work.

British Library Cataloguing in Publication Data
A catalogue record for this book is available from the British Library.

Edited by Mark Jordan
Picture research by Caroline Thompson
Design by Chi Leung
Commissioning Editor: Alison Walters
Cover photographs: Tony Stone Images, Andrew Lambert
Illustrations by Barking Dog Art, Russell Birkett, Phillip Burrows, Peter Harper,
Illustrated Arts, Bethan Matthews, Sylvie Poggio Agency (Nick Duffy)
and Harry Venning
Production by James Graves
Printed and bound by Scotprint, Musselburgh.

Module F1

Number and algebra

❶ Estimating tenths

Reading scales and estimating amounts to one decimal place on marked and unmarked scales

❷ Multiplying and dividing by 10, 100 and 1000

Solving problems by multiplying or dividing a whole number by 10, 100 or 1000

❸ Comparing decimals

Comparing decimal numbers with one or two decimal places. Recognising that the number of digits is less important than the place value of the digits

❹ How many quarters?

Adding and subtracting multiples of halves and quarters

❺ Writing fractions

Identifying $\frac{x}{y}$ in both practical and everyday contexts

❻ Percentage scales

Using a percentage scale from 0% to 100%. Linking simple percentages to fractions

Key words and phrases

decimal
estimate
one tenth

powers of 10
times by 10, 100 and 1000
two decimal places

half
one and a half
quarter
three-quarters
two and a quarter

fraction
in each 100
per cent

① **Estimating tenths**

Champion tennis players have a powerful serve. The speed that the ball travels is measured in miles per hour and displayed for the crowd to see. Sometimes the speed is measured to one decimal place. How accurate do you think these speed measurements are?

Can you think of any other sports where the speed of a ball or the speed of people are recorded?

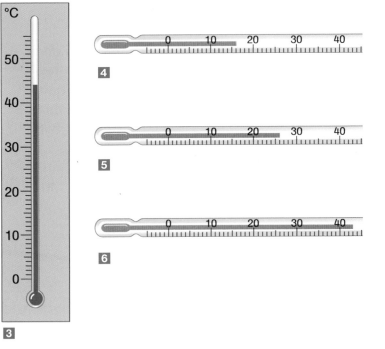

Miles per hour
`888118.500`

A Look at these thermometers and write down the temperatures that they show.

1

2

3

4

5

6

B Measure these lines and write down their lengths to the nearest tenth of a centimetre.

1 [line]   4 [line]

2 [line]   5 [line]

3 [line]   6 [line]

C This line is 10 units long.

```
0                                              10
|——————————————————————————————————————————————|
        b              a        d        c
```

The letters on the line represent different numbers of units.

1 Complete the table.

Letter	Number of units
a	5
b	☆
c	☆
d	☆

D This line is 15 cm long. Copy the line and then estimate where to draw these values on the line.

0%   100%
```
|——————————————————————————————————————————————|
```

1 51%   3 80%   5 62%
2 25%   4 98%   6 75%

E Look at the line and estimate the value of each of the letters labelled **a** to **f**.

0%   100%
```
|——————————————————————————————————————————————|
      ↑         ↑      ↑↑            ↑              ↑
      e         b      f c           a              d
```

1 a = ?   3 c = ?   5 e = ?
2 b = ?   4 d = ?   6 f = ?

Now look back at your work in this lesson.
- Can you find a point on a line that is 4/10 of its length?
- Try drawing some lines of different lengths and then mark 0%, 25%, 50%, 75% and 100% at the right points along each line.

② Multiplying and dividing by 10, 100 and 1000

Charities collect ten times more money now than they did 20 years ago.
What charity events have you watched or taken part in?
What is the relationship between *times 10* and *times 100*?

A local shopkeeper is helping to raise money for a new school minibus. For every £10 that the school raises, he promises to pay £1 into the fund. How much will the shopkeeper pay at the end of each of the following weeks?

1 In the first week the school raises £70.
2 In the second week the school raises £90.
3 In the third week the school raises £60.
4 In the fourth week the school raises £80.
5 In the fifth week the school raises £40.
6 In the sixth week the school raises £110.

Complete these number patterns.

1 30, ✪, 50, ✪, 70
2 200, 300, ✪, 500, ✪, 700
3 90, 80, ✪, 60, 50, ✪
4 800, ✪, 600, 500, ✪, 300
5 ✪, 40, 50, 60, ✪, 80
6 ✪, ✪, 600, 500, 400, 300

Jackie has to fill boxes with candles. Each box holds 100 candles and she can only pack boxes that will be completely filled. Any leftover candles are put on one side. Answer these questions.

1 On Monday she has 400 candles. How many boxes will she fill?
2 On Tuesday she has 620 candles. How many boxes will she fill?
3 On Wednesday she has 710 candles. How many boxes will she fill?
4 On Thursday she has 420 candles. How many boxes will she fill?
5 On Friday she has 560 candles. How many boxes will she fill?
6 On Saturday she has 340 candles. How many boxes will she fill?

D Copy and complete this table.

	×10	×100	×1000
5	50		
7		700	
8			8000
6			
10			
20			

E Six children collected 1p coins for a local charity. One shopkeeper offered to exchange every 100 pence with a £1 coin, and then give an extra 10 pence piece for each pound collected.

1 Simon has 542p. How many £1 coins will he receive from the shopkeeper? How many 10 pence pieces will he receive?

2 Tracy has 326p. How many £1 coins will she receive from the shopkeeper? How many pennies will she be left with?

3 Anna has 620p. If she gives the shopkeeper 600 pennies, what will he give her in return?

4 Susie has 417p. She received £4 and 40p from the shopkeeper. How much money did she collect in total?

5 Jimmy has 1224p. How many £1 coins will he receive from the shopkeeper? How much will the shopkeeper give him in total?

6 Jane has 475p. After visiting the shopkeeper, what coins will she have?

Now look back at your work in this lesson.
- What are the quick ways to multiply by 10 and by 100?
- What type of numbers can be divided by 10 to leave a whole number as the answer?

③ Comparing decimals

This is Ed de Goey, a goalkeeper for Chelsea and Holland. He is 1.97 metres tall and is the tallest player in Chelsea's history. How much higher do you think the crossbar is? Which sports have the tallest players?

Here are the heights of some pairs of pupils in Jackie's class. Write in your book which of each pair is taller.
1. Jackie 1.47 m   Angela 1.5 m
2. Hanif 1.62 m   Wayne 1.59 m
3. Robert 1.44 m   Jenny 1.52 m
4. John 1.71 m   Chris 1.68 m
5. Who is the tallest out of all these pupils?
6. Who is the shortest out of all these pupils?

In each question, put the numbers in order, starting with the smallest.
1. 1.46, 1.43, 1.39, 1.5
2. 2.14, 2.05, 2.22, 2.12
3. 8.61, 8.56, 8.72, 8.04
4. 5.94, 6.12, 5.98, 6.34
5. 7.00, 6.95, 7.48, 6.67
6. 22.81, 23.01, 22.85, 23.07

Wasim and his friends do Saturday jobs. Their hourly rates of pay are shown below. Who earns the highest rate in each group?
1. Wasim £3.54, John £3.48, Steve £3.50
2. Fahema £3.61, Joanne £3.45, Debbie £3.60
3. Alan £3.82, Bill £3.80, Ritesh £3.90
4. Simon £3.26, Winston £3.35, Ruth £3.30
5. Who gets the highest hourly rate in the whole group?
6. Who gets the lowest hourly rate in the whole group?

D

Anna and Sandra work in a cattery. There are three of each type of cat. They weigh them each month and record their weight. Which is the heaviest of each set of cats?

1 Siamese
Prudence 1.54 kilograms, Lady 1.6 kilograms, George 1.68 kilograms

2 Chinchilla
Fluffy 2.03 kilograms, Tina 2.59 kilograms, Victoria 2.46 kilograms

3 Tabby
Samantha 1.86 kilograms, Tiddles 2.1 kilograms, Tabitha 2.45 kilograms

4 Tortoiseshell
Tiger 2.34 kilograms, Isabella 2.24 kilograms, Spencer 2.39 kilograms

5 Black
Gremlin 3.1 kilograms, Bonzo 2.88 kilograms, Ratbag 2.9 kilograms

6 Ginger
Psycho 2.42 kilograms, Ginge 2.38 kilograms, Geri 2.41 kilograms

E

Find three different types of pen that have tops. For each pen, measure:
- the length of the top only
- the length of pen only
- the length of the pen when the top is fully in place.

Use a table to record your measurements in centimetres, writing the millimetres as a decimal.

Pen	Top only	Pen only	Pen with top
a			
b			
c			

1 Which pen has the longest top?
2 Which top adds most to the total length of the pen?

Now look back at your work in this lesson.
- How can a two-digit number such as 1.6 be bigger than a three-digit number such as 1.45?
- What things can be measured to two decimal places?

④ How many quarters?

On school visits around this chocolate factory, everyone is given half a bar of chocolate as a present. If there were 25 people on a visit, how many whole bars of chocolate would the factory need to give away?

Here are three chocolate bars. Answer these questions about them.

Chocolate Delight

Nut Bar

Giant Bar

1 John eats ½ a bar of Chocolate Delight and Debbie eats ¾ of the same type of bar. What fraction of Chocolate Delight bars do they eat in total?

2 Hanif eats 1¼ bars of Chocolate Delight and Winston eats ¼ of the same bar of chocolate. How many squares do they eat between them?
Using fractions, how many chocolate bars have they eaten?

3 Sandra eats ¼ of a Nut bar. Chris eats ¾ of the same type of bar. How many Nut bars have they eaten between them?

4 Jane and Joanne each eat ½ of a Nut bar. How much of the Nut bar have they eaten between them?

5 Wasim eats ½ of a Giant bar. Mark eats ¼ of the same Giant bar. How much of the Giant bar have they eaten between them?

6 Abdul, Fahema, Colin and Jason each eat ¼ of a Giant bar. How many squares do each of them eat?
How much of the Giant bar have they eaten in total?

Work out the answers to these questions.

1 ¾ + ¼ = ⊚

2 ½ + ¼ = ⊚

3 ½ + ½ = ⊚

4 ¾ − ¼ = ⊚

5 ¾ − ½ = ⊚

6 1 − ½ = ⊚

Vic and Sal decided to make a fruit salad. They made a list of what they needed, but by mistake they both bought same fruit. Complete this table to show the total amount of fruit they bought.

Vic's fruit	Sal's fruit	Total amount
1 ½ lb plums	1 lb plums	
2 ½ lb apricots	½ lb apricots	
3 ¾ lb strawberries	1 lb strawberries	
4 ½ lb cherries	¾ lb cherries	
5 ¾ lb raspberries	½ lb raspberries	
6 1 lb blackcurrants	½ lb blackcurrants	

Rob and Amy check their stock of refreshments before the youth club opens and check them again after the youth club has closed. Look at their findings and answer these questions.

1 They start with ¾ of a box of crisps and sell ½ a box. What fraction of the box of crisps is left?

2 They start with 1½ box of nuts and sell 1 box. What fraction is left?

3 They start with 1¼ box of chocolate bars and sell ¾ of a box. What fraction is left?

4 They start with 5 full pizzas and sell 3½ pizzas. What fraction is left?

5 They start with ½ a box of cans of lemonade and sell ½ of the cans. What fraction of a box is left?

6 They start with ¾ of a box of packets of sweets and end up with ¼ of a box. What fraction of a box did they sell?

Joanne and her friends are saving stamps to get gifts from a catalogue. They pair up their collections and then share the gift. Work out how many books each pair of girls have.

1 Joanne has 1½ books and Debbie has 1¼ books. How many books do they have altogether?

2 Sandra has 2¾ books and Ann has ½ a book. How many books do they have altogether?

3 Emma has 1½ books and Angie has 4½ books. How many books do they have altogether?

4 Jill has ¾ of a book and Sonia has 5¼ books. How many books do they have altogether?

5 Sue has 10¾ books and Vicky has ¾ of a book. How many books do they have altogether?

6 Jane has 2¼ books and Andrea has 12½ books. How many books do they have altogether?

Now look back at your work in this lesson.
- How do you add numbers that include halves and quarters?
- Write down three pairs of fractions that add up to 1.

⑤ Writing fractions

Hollywood Chicken Farm specialises in exotic eggs used in top restaurants.
Do you think all types of chicken lay the same number of eggs each day?
What size egg boxes have you seen in supermarkets?

Jackie works at Hollywood Farm collecting eggs and putting
them into egg boxes. There are different size egg boxes for
different types of egg.

At the end of the day, if a box is half filled or more, it is sent
to the restaurant. For each of the boxes below, write down the
fraction filled, and say if it will be sent to the restaurant.

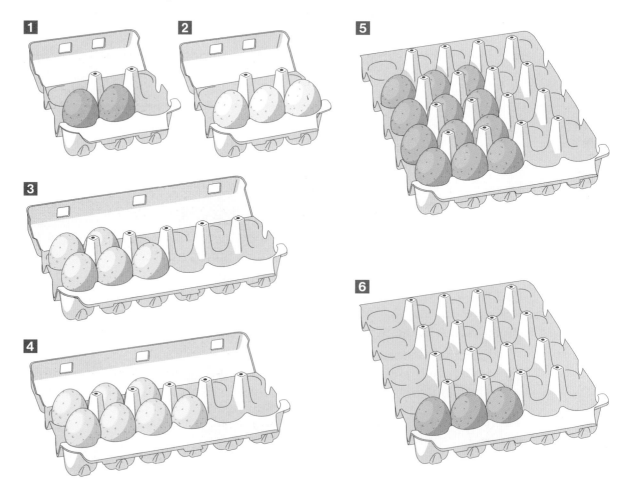

Sean and his friends buy different kinds of chocolate bars. Work out what fraction of their bar of chocolate each of them has eaten.

1. Sean's bar has four fingers and he eats three of them. What fraction has he eaten?

2. Jane's chocolate bar has six fingers within one wrapper. She eats one of them. What fraction of the bar has she eaten? If she eats the same fraction each day, how many days will the bar last?

3. Debbie has a pack of eight chocolate mints. She eats two of them. What fraction has she eaten? If she eats the same fraction each day, how many days will the pack last?

4. Wayne has a bar of chocolate with eight pieces. He eats three of them. What fraction has he eaten? If he eats the same fraction the next day, how many pieces will he have leftover?

5. Shripa has a bar of chocolate with 12 pieces. She eats nine of them. What fraction has she eaten?

6. Bill has a bar of chocolate with 16 pieces. He eats five of them. What fraction has he eaten? If he eats the same fraction on the next two days, how many pieces will be left?

1. Vicky goes to aerobics classes on Mondays, Tuesdays and Saturdays. What fraction of a week is this?
2. John and Debbie go to a disco on Fridays and Saturdays. What fraction of a week is this?
3. Hanif and Sam go to a judo club on Wednesdays. What fraction of a week is this?

A school week is usually Monday to Friday (five days). Think about this for the following questions.

4. Jason and Winston do football training after school on Mondays, Tuesdays and Fridays. What fraction of a school week is this?
5. Gustavo's class has swimming every Friday. What fraction of a school week is this?
6. Londa's class has Maths on Monday, Tuesday, Wednesday and Friday. What fraction of a school week is this?

D For each of these patterns, write down the fraction that has been shaded in a darker colour.

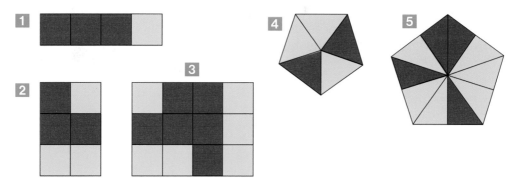

E Six friends decided to find out which pets are most popular with pupils at their school. Each of them asked a different group of pupils in the playground. Then they compared the fractions.

1 Peter asked five pupils, and three of them had a cat. What fraction of the group is this?

2 Sandra asked seven pupils if they had a dog, and three of them did. What fraction of the group is this?

3 Faiza asked eight pupils if they had a parrot, and one of them did. What fraction of the group is this?

4 Paul asked six pupils if they had a goldfish, and two of them did. What fraction of the group is this?

5 In Wayne's group of nine pupils, four of them had a budgie. What fraction of the group is this?

6 In Amy's group of ten pupils, six of them had a rabbit. What fraction of the group is this?

Now look back at your work in this lesson.
- Can you write fractions to represent '3 out of 4', and '7 out of 10'?
- How do you tell if a fraction is more or less than ½?

⑥ Percentage scales

This family keep in touch via their computer. Even though they are half way across the world from each other they can see each other to say hello! It is estimated that by the year 2001, 73% of homes will have computers. Is that more than half of all homes, or less than half?
How many of the people in your class have used a computer? Write this as a percentage.
What does *per cent* mean?

Carol carries out a survey of her class to find out what machines they have at home. Answers these questions about her results.

1. Three-quarters of the pupils have a video recorder. What percentage is this?
2. All of them have a television. What percentage is this?
3. One in four of them has a dishwasher. What percentage is this?
4. Half of them have a mobile phone. What percentage is this?
5. One in four of them has an answerphone. What percentage is this?
6. Four out of every ten have a computer. What percentage is this?

Look at the following fractions and percentages. In each case, write down which amount is greater.

1. ½ or 60%
2. ¼ or 40 %
3. ¾ or 70%
4. ⁹⁄₁₀ or 100%
5. ¼ or 20%
6. ⅓ or 25%

C

Mandy's jogging group runs five laps around the local park every week. They think of the run in terms of percentages. Use these percentages to help you answer the following questions.

0%	10%	20%	30%	40%	50%	60%	70%	80%	90%	100%
Start										Finish

1 After one lap, what percentage of the race have they completed?
2 After one lap, what percentage of the race do they still have to run?
3 After three laps, what percentage of the race have they completed?
4 After two laps, what percentage of the race have they completed?
5 After two laps, what percentage of the race do they still have to run?
6 After four laps, what percentage of the race have they completed?

D

Sandra's class are doing a Maths exam which lasts for one hour. Answer these questions by choosing from the following percentages.

0%	15%	25%	35%	50%	65%	75%	100%

1 After 15 minutes, what percentage of the time has been *used*?
2 After 15 minutes, what percentage of the time *remains*?
3 After 45 minutes, what percentage of the time has been *used*?
4 After 45 minutes, what percentage of the time *remains*?
5 After 60 minutes, what percentage of the time has been *used*?
6 After 30 minutes, what percentage of the time has been *used*?

E

Angus conducts a survey to find out how members of his class travel to school.
1 What percentage either walk or travel by car?
2 What percentage either walk or travel by bus?
3 What percentage either travel by car or by bus?
4 What percentage neither walk nor travel by bus?
5 What percentage neither travel by car nor by train?
6 What percentage do not walk to the school?

10% travel by train
30% travel by car
25% travel by bus
35% walk to school.

Now look back at your work in this lesson.
- How do you convert fractions into percentages?
- How do you add or subtract percentages?

Handling data

1 Two-step coding
Using a coding system with at least two symbols, which can be used to find or store items

2 Conversion graphs
Using graphs to convert from one set of units to another

3 Plotting decimals
Plotting or reading data to one decimal place in graphs

4 Time and distance graphs
Reading continuous graphs of time and distance

5 Charting data by intervals
Working with histograms over suitable intervals to organise a large amount of data into useful groups

6 Organising data
Practising coding and graphical skills learnt from the previous five lessons

Key words and phrases

code
continuous
equivalent
exchange
label
line
periods of time
plot
position
represent
slope
symbol

bar chart
equal and unequal intervals
grouping data in intervals
histogram
misleading

overall range
range of data within a group
tally

① Two-step coding

How do you find your seat in a theatre?
Usually, your ticket has a letter to tell you
which row to go to, and a number telling
you how far along the row you have to walk.
Have you been to an event with a ticket
with your seat number?

The front six rows of the Classic theatre are coded from A to F.
Each row has ten seats numbered from 1 to 10. The ticket for the
third seat in row F has the code F3. Work out the code written
on the tickets for each of the six blue seats.

Stage

A

B

C

D

E

F 1 2 3

In Jenny's school, the classes are known by a system that uses
the year they are in and the initial of their form teacher's name.
Jenny is in class 9K, Robert is in class 8T, Matt is in class 7B and
Alam is in class 9P.

The form teachers in their part of the school are:

| Mr Kenton | Mrs Bolton | Miss Reynolds | Mr Tanner |
| Mr Cragg | Miss Patel | | |

1 Are any of these pupils in the same class?
2 Are any of them in the same year?
3 Whose class do you think Alam is in?
4 Which year is Mrs Bolton's class?
5 Jameela is in Mr Cragg's class. She is year 8. Which class is
she in?
6 Who is in the same year as Jameela?

The Carlton Hotel has six floors. The ground floor is floor 0 and the top floor is floor 5.

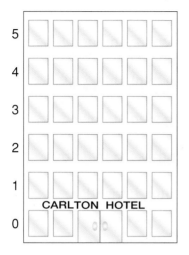

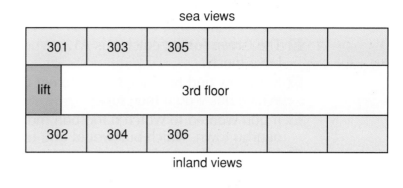

On each floor, rooms are numbered starting by the lift, first with the floor number and then the room number. Room 410 is on the fourth floor and is room 10 on that floor. Even-numbered rooms have inland views and odd-numbered rooms have sea views.

1 What view do you get from room 410?
2 Which rooms have a sea view on the top floor?
3 Which two rooms are next to the lift on the second floor?
4 Mr and Mrs Musana have room 105. Which floor are they on? Do they have a sea view?
5 Which rooms are above and below room 306?
6 Which room with an inland view is fourth from the lift on floor 3?

D

There is a small library on the ground floor of the hotel. The books are divided into sections. Some of the sections are written below.

Romance	Adventure	Travel	Spy stories	Places to visit

When a guest wants to borrow a book, they write down a record of their room number followed by the first two letters of the section. So when the person in room 303 borrows a travel book, they write down 303TR.
Fill in the code for the following books.
1 A romance for Mrs Smith in room 210.
2 A spy story for Miss Sands in room 502.
3 *Exploring Our Town*, a book on local places for Mr Kahn in room 406
4 *Adventures of the East* for Tom in room 101.
5 The person in room 403 writes down 403TH. What other section might this book come from?

E

Outside the hotel are three sorts of buses.
A buses go round the town.
B buses visit nearby towns
C buses travel long distances.
Each bus travels four times a day at 9 a.m., 12 noon, 3 p.m. and 6 p.m.

1 Mr and Mrs Fogg catch bus C9. Where might they be going?

2 The Green family catch bus A12. Where do you think they will have lunch?

3 Miss Low and her friend want to eat an evening meal in town. Which bus would they take?

4 If you wanted to watch a football match starting at 2 p.m. in a nearby town, which bus would you take?

5 Jason and Greg want to spend the morning visiting a friend in the next town. Choose a bus for them to use.

F

In the hotel car park the cars are parked in four rows with 15 spaces in each row. Every guest has their own space which is given to them when they arrive. Work out a code for each space, showing the row and the distance from the end so each guest can find their space easily.

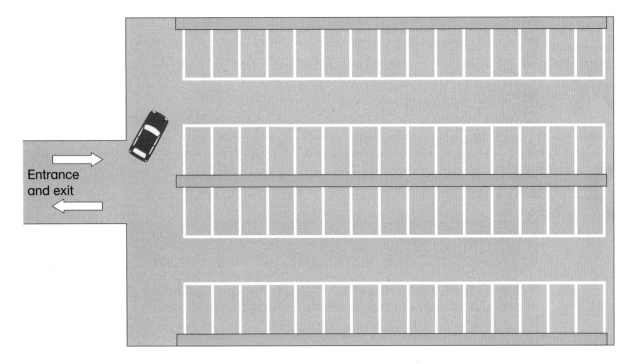

Entrance
and exit

Now look back at your work in this lesson.
- Think of three places where you can use a coding system to find something.
- Make up a coding system to help people find their seats easily for a school play.

Conversion graphs

When you buy something in another country, most people compare the price with what it would cost in pounds. In Italy, people buy things using *lira*. Spending 2000 lira on an ice cream may sound like a fortune, but it's actually worth less than £1.

Davide is a French boy visiting England. He goes the market to buy some vegetables. Most stalls weigh their vegetables by the pound, but he is used to kilograms. Davide remembers that 2 pounds weigh roughly 1 kilogram, so he draws a conversion graph to remind him how to change pounds approximately into kilograms.

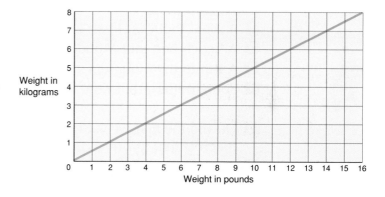

Find out from Davide's graph approximately how many kilograms are the same as the following weights in pounds.

1. 16 pounds
2. 12 pounds
3. 8 pounds
4. 6 pounds
5. 7 pounds
6. 13 pounds

Now use the graph to find how many pounds are the same as these amounts of kilograms.

1. 8 kg
2. 5 kg
3. 3 kg
4. 6 kg
5. 4 ½ kg
6. 2 ½ kg

Here is a conversion graph that shows how many Cypriot pounds you get in exchange for British pounds.

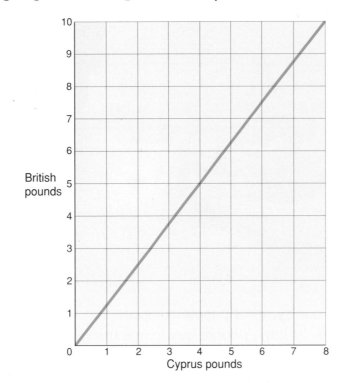

Mandy and Kate are spending their holiday in Cyprus this year. Use the graph to find out what the following items cost them in British pounds.

1 A meal that cost them 20 Cyprus pounds
2 A beach bag that Mandy bought for 15 Cyprus pounds
3 A trip to the mountain villages that cost 30 Cyprus pounds
4 Some pottery that Kate bought for 50 Cyprus pounds

5 During the first week Kate spent 100 Cyprus pounds. How much is that in British pounds?
6 Mandy ran out of cash, so she changed another £50 into Cyprus pounds. How man Cyprus pounds would she get?

Stavros lives in Cyprus. He came to England to spend two weeks with his uncle. He had saved 120 Cyprus pounds to spend on his holiday.

1 How many British pounds would he get to spend?
2 He spent £25 on a night at the theatre. How much is that in Cyprus pounds?
3 The presents for his family at home cost £40 in London. How many Cyprus pounds did he spend on presents?
4 During his holiday he also spent £35 pounds on snacks and £20 on other items. How many British pounds did he have left at the end of his holiday?
5 How much would that be worth when he got home?

E

When Barry told his grandmother that he was now 175 cm tall, she looked blank. Barry's grandmother still measures things in inches. He knew that 10 inches measure roughly 25 cm. Using this conversion, Barry drew a graph to show her how to change centimetres into inches.

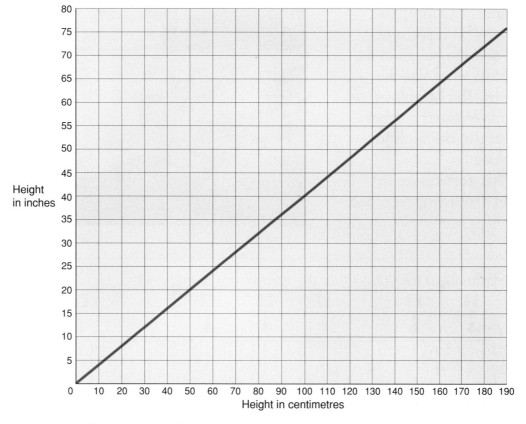

Use the graph to answer these questions.

1 What is Barry's height in inches?

2 There are 12 inches in 1 foot. Write Barry's height in feet and inches.

3 Barry's sister is 150 cm tall. What is this in inches?

4 His older brother is 180 cm. Write his height in feet and inches.

F

Barry's grandmother knows the heights of her family in feet and inches. Use the graph to find their heights in centimetres.

1 Barry's grandmother is 5 ft 2 in.

2 Uncle Robert is 5 ft 8 in.

3 Aunt Ruth is 4 ft 10 in.

4 Cousin Alec is 5 ft.

5 Which relation is about the same height as Barry?

Now look back at your work in this lesson.
- Make a list of things that need converting from one set of units to another.
- Draw your own conversion graph for one of these ideas.

③ Plotting decimals

Scientists study earthquakes using special machines. The machines record vibrations on a piece of graph paper and the height of the lines tell scientists what size the earthquake was. The heights of the lines are never exact numbers, so the scientists use decimals to record the values.

The value of this earthquake in Los Angeles in 1994 was recorded as 6.7.

A Write down the values that the arrows are pointing to.

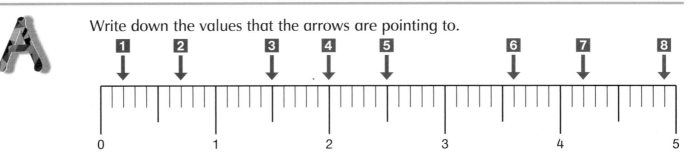

B Write down the values that the arrows are pointing to on this vertical line.

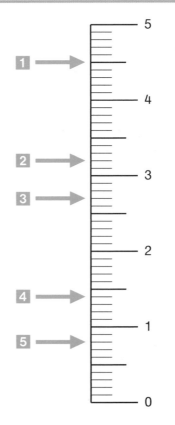

Jameela has flu. Her temperature went up in the morning but after taking some medicine it gradually went down in the afternoon.

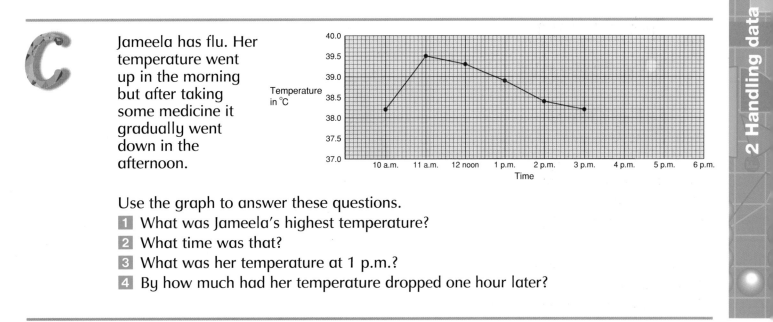

Use the graph to answer these questions.
1. What was Jameela's highest temperature?
2. What time was that?
3. What was her temperature at 1 p.m.?
4. By how much had her temperature dropped one hour later?

Copy Jameela's temperature graph onto graph paper. Add these points to your graph and draw in the lines.
1. At 4 p.m. her temperature was 37.5 °C.
2. At 5 p.m. her temperature was 37.2 °C.
3. At 6 p.m. her temperature was 37.0 °C.

John, Jodie, Eric, Ella, Babs and Isaac measured their heights at the beginning of 1998 and again one year later. They recorded the results on a double bar chart to show how much they had grown in a year.

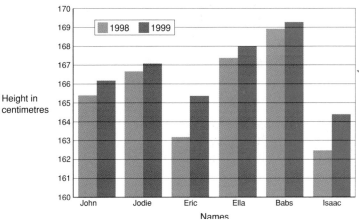

1. Who was the tallest in 1998?
2. Was the same person still tallest the following year?
3. Which of them grew the most in the year?
4. Did Ella grow more or less than John?
5. If John grows the same amount in the following year, how tall will he be in 2000?
6. If Eric grew the same amount again by 2000, would he be taller than John?

Now look back at your work in this lesson.
- Write down the steps you took to draw your graph with decimal measures.
- Look at the graphs in exercises C and E. For each graph, do you know how much each little step is worth on the vertical axis?

④ Time and distance graphs

Graphs and charts can show what is happening over a period of time during a journey. They can show how fast you are travelling and when you pause for a rest. They can also show when you reach your destination and at what point the return journey starts. Graphs can also show things like change in temperatures with time.

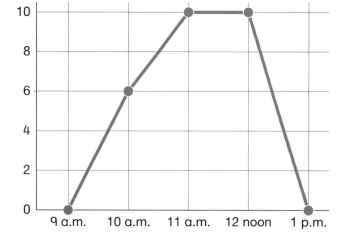

This graph shows a bike ride that Frances did in her school holiday.

10
8
6
4
2
0
9 a.m. 10 a.m. 11 a.m. 12 noon 1 p.m.

1 What do you think the numbers on the vertical axis represent?
2 Give the graph a title and a label for each of the axes.

Look again at the graph in Exercise A.
1 How far did Frances cycle in the first hour?
2 Did she travel further or less far in the second hour?
3 Can you think of a reason why she cycled more slowly in the second hour?
4 What can you say about her journey between 11 a.m. and 12 noon?
5 On her return journey, did she take more or less time than before?
6 Think of a reason that could explain this.

C This graph shows the water level in the bath when Jez had a good soak before bed.

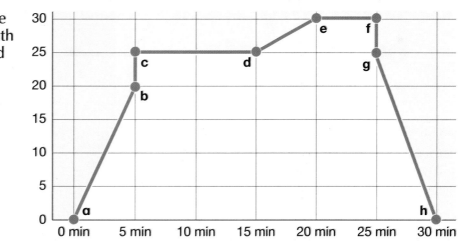

1 Suggest labels for the axes.
2 How long did the bath take to fill?
3 Why do you think the water level rose between **b** and **c**?
4 Jez relaxed in the bath between **c** and **d** and then found that the water was getting cold.
   What do you think he did from d to e?
5 Describe what was happening between **e** and **g**.
6 How long did the bath take to empty?

D This graph shows the walk that Rufus and his friends did to get from one youth hostel to another during a walking holiday.

1 Suggest labels for the two axes in this graph.
2 Rufus dropped his map fairly near the beginning of the journey. Can you tell from the graph at what time he discovered this?
3 How far did he walk back before he found it?
4 Seven miles along their journey was an interesting area with caves to explore. What time did they arrive there?
5 What time did they arrive at the next hostel?
6 How long did the whole journey take?

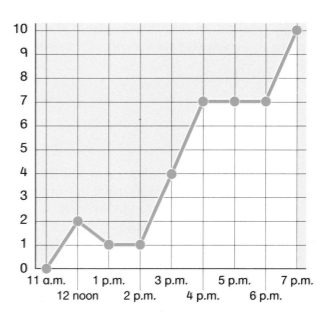

Now look back at your work in this lesson.
• Do you need values on both axes to tell the story of a journey?
• Is one axis more important than the other?

⑤ Charting data by intervals

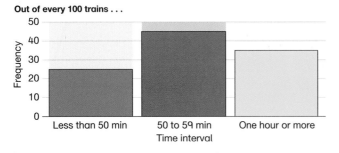

Out of every 100 trains . . .

The train company promises that most journeys from John's town to London will take less than one hour. This histogram shows how that promise was kept last year. How many trains out of every 100 made the journey in between 50 and 59 minutes? How many trains in every 100 took less than one hour? Do you think that the intervals in this chart are misleading?

 John's father travels to London daily, and he complains that he is sometimes very late to work.

So John's father recorded the length of his journey in minutes each day for eight weeks.

Week	Mon	Tues	Wed	Thurs	Fri
Week 1	45	68	38	74	38
Week 2	64	39	55	48	56
Week 3	55	55	81	73	68
Week 4	54	48	36	62	55
Week 5	72	56	43	44	39
Week 6	48	39	48	43	54
Week 7	45	53	47	67	63
Week 8	55	61	73	76	78

Answer these questions.

1 What was the shortest journey time?
2 On how many days did the journey take more than 75 minutes?
3 What was the longest journey time?
4 In which week was this journey?

B Make a new list of the train times given in exercise A. For each week, write the journey times in order starting with the shortest time. Remember to include all the times, even when some are the same.

C Use your list from exercise B to answer these questions.
1. The *range* is the difference between the longest and the shortest journey in a week. What is the range of the journey times in week 1?
2. Write down the range for each of the other seven weeks.
3. What is the range over all eight weeks?
4. Why do you think the overall range is bigger than the ranges in individual weeks?
5. Do you think it would be suitable to draw a bar chart of this data? Give your reasons.

D Copy this table and use a tally to find the total over each interval.

Time interval	Tally	Total
Less than 50 minutes		
50–59 minutes		
One hour or more		

E Draw a histogram with this data.
Look at the histogram at the start of this lesson if you need some help.

F Now answer these questions using your own histogram.
1. Is the train company's claim that 'most trains make the journey in less than one hour' true or false? How do you show that?
2. Give two reasons why your histogram is different from the train company's histogram?

Now look back at your work in this lesson.
- What are the benefits of using intervals to chart data?
- What are the differences between bar charts and histograms?

⑥ Organising data

In cities, residents from different buildings often share the same car parks.
How can they avoid arguments about sharing the parking spaces fairly?

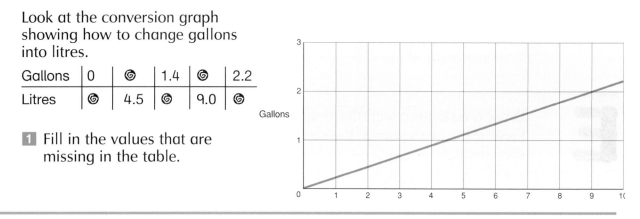

At the end of Sarah's road there are three blocks of flats: Oak House, Elm House and Chestnut House. There are twelve flats in each block. The car park nearby is shared by the residents from all the flats and each flat has one space for parking. Work out a numbering system for the parking spaces so that each resident knows where to put their car.

Look at the conversion graph showing how to change gallons into litres.

Gallons	0	🌀	1.4	🌀	2.2
Litres	🌀	4.5	🌀	9.0	🌀

1 Fill in the values that are missing in the table.

Gallons

This chart shows the distances that some cricketers could throw a ball during fielding practice.

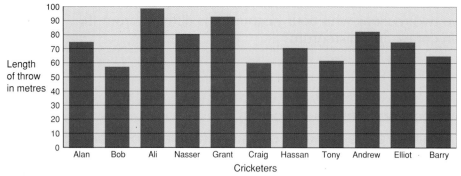

1 Make a list of all the cricketers with the distance each one could throw.

2 Who threw the ball furthest?

3 Who had the shortest throw that day?

4 What is the range of these values?

Karen's family drove 200 miles to their holiday home. Here is a graph to show their journey.

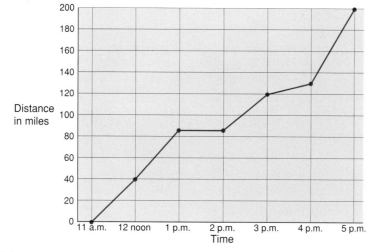

1 How far did they travel in the first hour?

2 How far had they gone after two hours?

3 Was their average speed faster or slower in the second hour?

4 What do you think that they could have been doing between 1 p.m. and 2 p.m.?

5 Can you think of a reason why they covered so little distance between 3 and 4 o'clock?

6 Which part of the journey was on a motorway?

What time did you get up this morning?

Samira asked all the pupils in her class that question. Here are their replies.

7:00	7:12	8:05	8:10	7:43	7:35
7:14	7:39	7:37	8:05	7:24	7:15
7:45	7:10	7:50	7:55	6:55	6:38
6:30	6:48	7:23	6:10	8:10	7:14
6:37	6:54	7:09	7:35	7:18	7:12

1 Sort the times into suitable, equal, time intervals, making sure that they do not overlap.

2 Label a horizontal axis to show the time from 6 a.m. to 8:30 a.m. and mark in your chosen intervals.

3 Add a vertical axis to show the number of pupils in each interval.

4 Draw a bar graph to show the number of pupils that got up in each time interval.

Now look back at your work in this lesson.
- Write down all the types of graphs and charts you have used in this chapter.
- Add some notes to remind you how to use each type of graph.

Number and algebra

1 **In your head or on paper**
Solving a problem by adding or subtracting two-digit numbers without a calculator

2 **Multiplying two-digit and one-digit numbers**
Solving problems by multiplying a two-digit number by a one-digit number, without using a calculator

3 **Two-step calculations**
Solving problems which require two operations, such as addition and then multiplication, using whole numbers

4 **Which number to start with?**
Realising that the order in which you multiply numbers does not affect the answer. Finding the easiest way to solve multiplication problems

5 **More of this, less of that**
Understanding inverse proportion relationships. Seeing that increasing one amount can reduce another amount

6 **One in four, one quarter**
Finding a single fraction, such as $\frac{1}{3}$, of a number that is easily divisible

Key words and phrases

altogether	balance
discount	describe the rule
pays in	inverse
total	multiply
withdraws	operation
	overdrawn
	product
	sum of

❶ In your head or on paper

The turtle probably lives to the greatest age of any creature. Some turtles have lived for 152 years!
The person with the longest recorded life was a Japanese man who was born on 29 June 1865 and died on 21 February 1986 – a life span of 120 years, 237 days. Would you like to live for over 100 years?
Which other animals have a long life span?

Jason and his friends were arguing over who has the oldest parents.
So they each told Jason the ages of their parents and he added the two numbers to find their combined age. Answer these questions.

1 Jason's parents are 34 and 39. What is their combined age?
2 Fahema's parents are 36 and 38. What is their combined age?
3 Roberto's parents are 44 and 49. What is their combined age?
4 Jane's parents are 32 and 39. What is their combined age?
5 Angie's parents are 45 and 46. What is their combined age?
6 Who has got the oldest parents? Who has got the youngest parents?

B

Look at these questions and write down the answers.
1 98 + 42   **4** 82 + 125
2 196 − 24   **5** 243 − 123
3 127 + 132   **6** 251 + 252

C

Roger and his friends have been saving their money. All of them have accounts with the Post Office. Work out their new balance after these changes.

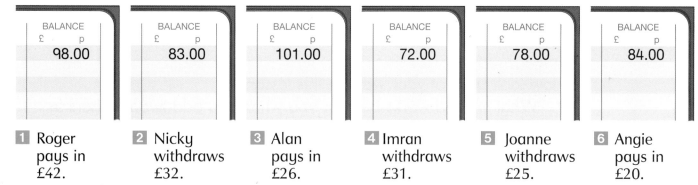

BALANCE £ p	BALANCE £ p	BALANCE £ p	BALANCE £ p	BALANCE £ p	BALANCE £ p
98.00	83.00	101.00	72.00	78.00	84.00

1 Roger pays in £42.
2 Nicky withdraws £32.
3 Alan pays in £26.
4 Imran withdraws £31.
5 Joanne withdraws £25.
6 Angie pays in £20.

D Gary and his friends work during the school holidays. In their last week they each receive a bonus. Work out the total amount each of them earns.

1 Gary earns £258 and gets a bonus of £42.
2 Melissa earns £210 and gets a bonus of £63.
3 Curtley earns £265 and gets a bonus of £45.
4 Anna earns £270 and gets a bonus of £35.

Catherine and George have to take the train to get to work.
Work out how much they are left with after paying for travel.

5 Catherine earns £252 and gets a bonus of £37. She pays £25 on train tickets.
6 George earns £240 and gets a bonus of £52. He pays £20 on train tickets.

E An election is held for the position of president at John's football club.

Most people voted at the club meeting, but some votes were sent in the post. Work out the total number of votes that each candidate received.

1 Alan Fisher received 228 votes and 62 postal votes.
2 Anna Weaver received 298 votes and 24 postal votes.
3 Patrick Farmer received 301 votes and 64 postal votes.

Two candidates had some votes discounted at the final check.
What was their overall total?

4 Bob Hunter received 312 votes and 57 postal votes. Twelve votes were discounted.
5 Linda Driver received 304 votes and 27 postal votes. Eight votes were discounted
6 Who won the election?

Now look back at your work in this lesson.
• What method works best for you when you add two numbers in your head?
• What method works best for you when you subtract two numbers in your head?

❷ Multiplying two-digit and one-digit numbers

This is a scene from a popular TV series. How long is each episode usually in this type of series? How many episodes are there usually each week? Can you work out how many hours the programme is on each week?
What is your favourite television programme?
How many hours a week do you spend watching it?

Each member of Alan's family has a different favourite TV programme. Work out how much time each member of the family spends watching their favourite programme per week.

1 Alan's favourite programme is 'The Bill'. He watches two episodes lasting 1 hour each every week.

2 His mum's favourite programme is 'Countdown'. She watches five programmes of 25 minutes every week.

3 His sister's favourite programme is 'The Ricky Lake Show'. She watches four shows of 35 minutes every week.

4 Grandpa's favourite programme is the 9 o'clock news. Last week he watched five bulletins. Two of the bulletins lasted half an hour each, one bulletin lasted 20 minutes, and one bulletin lasted 25 minutes.

5 His brother's favourite programme is 'EastEnders'. He watches three episodes of 30 minutes and the omnibus edition lasting 90 minutes.

6 His grandma's favourite programme is 'Coronation Street'. She watches three episodes of 30 minutes every week.

Write down the answers to these questions.

1 $5 \times 14 = $ ✸

2 $6 + 21 + 4 = $ ✸

3 $7 \times 19 = $ ✸

4 $4 \times 22 = $ ✸

5 $9 \times 12 = $ ✸

6 $6 \times 32 = $ ✸

C

Mr Brown is arranging a school outing. There is a problem with transport. Work out how many pupils can be moved in the following combinations of vehicles.

1. 15 cars, each with five passenger seats.
2. 21 cars, each with four passenger seats.
3. Three minibuses: one with 14 passenger seats, one with 13 passenger seats and one with 15 passenger seats.
4. 11 vans, each with six passenger seats.
5. Three coaches, each with 62 passenger seats.
6. Four train compartments, each with 48 seats.

D

Hanif works in an office. He sells groups of stamps.

How much would these sets of stamps cost?

1. eight stamps at 19p each
2. 25 stamps at 10p each
3. 25 stamps at 5p each
4. 48 stamps at 2p each
5. Two stamps at 26p each, one stamp of 50p, and ten stamps at 5p each
6. What is the total value of these stamps?

E

Courtney and his friends do part-time jobs. Work out how much each of them earns per week.

1. Courtney earns £5 per hour and works 25 hours every week.
2. Jo earns £9 per hour and works a ten-hour week.
3. Colin earns £8 per hour and works a 15-hour week.
4. Becky earns £7 per hour and works an 18-hour week.
5. Andrea earns £7 per hour. This week she worked four hours each day for five days.
6. Rob earns £6 per hour and works a 12-hour week.

Now look back at your work in this lesson.
- What is your preferred way of multiplying a two-digit number by a one-digit number? Do you usually multiply the tens number or the unit number first?
- Do you have any short cuts for multiplying some numbers?

❸ Two-step calculations

This *Scrabble* word – QUIZ – scores loads of points!
To work out its score, you have to do several steps.
The Z is worth 10 points, but it is being placed on a
double letter square. What is 10 points doubled?
Next you have to add to this value the other letter
scores. Q is worth 10, U is worth 1 and I is worth 1.
What is the score so far?
Finally, the word is on a *triple word* square, so you
multiply the score so far by 3. What is the total score?

Rachid and his friends are sending off for some computer games
by mail order.

Each game costs £35. An extra charge of £2.20 is made for postage
and packing, no matter how many games there are in the order.

How much do each of these orders cost?

1 Rachid orders one game.
2 Helen orders two games.
3 Debbie orders six games.

4 Ali orders seven games.
5 Jason orders five games.
6 Joanne orders four games.

Sandra and her class are taking exams. Work out how much
time each of them has left.

1 Sandra is doing a one-hour Maths exam. She took 23 minutes
to answer the first question and 20 minutes to do the next one.
How much time has she got left?

2 Winston is doing a two-hour History paper. His first three
questions took 27 minutes, 22 minutes and 18 minutes. How
much time has he got left?

3 Alan is doing a 1½-hour Biology paper. The first question
took 31 minutes and the second took 25 minutes. How much
time has he got left?

4 Rushna is doing a three-hour Chemistry paper. She has taken
40 minutes and 38 minutes to do two questions. How much
time has she got left?

5 Jane is doing a two-hour French exam. She has taken 18 minutes,
16 minutes and 20 minutes to answer the first three questions.
How much time has she got left?

6 Brian is doing a three-hour English paper. He has taken 27 minutes
and 25 minutes to answer two questions. How much time has
he got left?

C

Write down the answers to these questions.

1 $(3 \times 5) + 22$ **4** $(7 \times 5) - 12$

2 $(4 \times 8) + 7$ **5** $(9 \times 7) - 15$

3 $14 + (6 \times 4)$ **6** $(10 \times 8) - 22$

D

Vicky and her friends want to work out how much time they have left on some video tapes.

1 Vicky has a three-hour tape and she has taped three half-hour programmes. How much time is left on her tape?

2 Carlton has a two-hour tape and he has taped two 45-minute programmes. How much time is left on his tape?

3 Janet has a four-hour tape and she has taped two half-hour programmes and a one-hour programme. How much time is left on her tape?

4 Jerry has a three-hour tape. He has taped two half-hour programmes and one 45-minute programme. How much time is left on his tape?

5 Ruth has a four-hour tape. She has taped one two-hour programme and one 45-minute programme. How much time is left on her tape?

6 Rob has a two-hour tape. He tapes four half-hour programmes. How much time is left on his tape?

E

Simon and his friends are playing darts. Each dart can score single, double or triple depending on where it hits the board.

Add the scores of each of the following players and write the answers in your book.

1 Simon scores 17, double 12 and double 6.

2 Hassan scores triple 6, double 4 and 7.

3 Janice scores 18, double 20 and triple 2.

4 Debbie scores double 5, double 6 and 16.

5 Wayne scores triple 19, double 10 and 5.

6 Ben scores 17, double 7 and double 18.

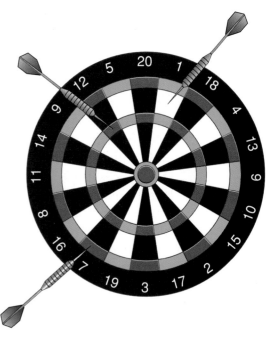

Now look back at your work in this lesson.
- Can you multiply two numbers in your head and then add another number? Practise a few calculations with your friends.
- What was the most useful skill you practised in this lesson?

④ Which number to start with?

This is Brian Lara. He scored 501 not out in one innings, which is a world record. It took him 7 hours and 54 minutes. How many minutes is that?

Some people think that cricket is a boring game because it is so slow. What do you think?

 Hanif and some of his friends play cricket for the school. He wants to work out the total number of runs that he has scored in the season. Write down the answers to these questions.

1 He scored 27 runs on three occasions. How many runs is this in total?

2 He scored 18 runs twice. How many runs is this?

3 In one match he scored 32 runs and on two occasions he scored 34. How many runs is this in total?

4 On four occasions he scored 16 runs. How many runs is this?

5 In the other matches, he scored 19 runs twice, 14, 5, 52 and 2. How many runs is this in total?

6 How many runs did he score altogether in the season?

 Look at the following pairs of sums and decide which one is easier to do in your head. Then write down the answers.

1 36×3 or 3×36
2 4×25 or 25×4
3 19×5 or 5×19
4 34×2 or 2×34
5 6×21 or 21×6
6 5×22 or 22×5

C

Sandra saves money by putting spare change in a jar. She wants to buy a computer game that costs £42.

Work out how much money Sandra has saved by completing the table below. The first has been done for you.

	Type of coin	Number	Total value
1	20p	6	£1.20
2	10p	18	
3	2p	34	
4	5p	15	
5	50p	24	
6	£2	14	

7 Has she saved enough money to buy the computer game?

D

Peter has a part-time job at a warehouse. He has to work out how many of each product is in stock.

Answer these questions.

1 There are 30 boxes of jars of pickle. Each box contains eight jars. How many jars are there altogether?

2 Each box of washing powder contains six packets. There are 20 full boxes and ten half-full boxes, each with only three packets each. How many packets are there altogether?

3 There are 20 boxes containing cans of cola. Each box contains 12 cans. How many cans are there altogether?

4 Each box contains four tins of biscuits. There are 32 boxes. How many tins are there altogether?

5 There are 40 boxes containing packets of corn flakes. Each box has six packets in it. How many packets are there altogether?

6 There are 30 boxes with packets of tea inside. Each box contains 12 packets. How many packets are there altogether?

Katy and her friends are going on a school journey for a week. They set their videos to record their favourite programmes. Work out if their tapes will be long enough.

1 Katy sets her video to record a 30-minute programme on four occasions. How long is this? Is her tape long enough?

2 Vicky sets her video to record a 55-minute programme on two occasions. How long is this? Is her tape long enough?

3 Martin sets his video to record a 1 hour 5 minute programme on three occasions. How long is this? Is his tape long enough?

4 Danielle sets her video to record a 45 minute programme on three occasions. How long is this? Is her tape long enough?

5 Jason sets his video to record a 25-minute programme on five occasions. How long is this? Is his tape long enough?

6 Justin his video to record a 1 hour 25 minute programme on three occasions. How long is this? Is his tape long enough?

Now look back at your work in this lesson.
- Do you find it easier sometimes to reverse the order of numbers that you are multiplying?
- Write a summary of things that you learnt this lesson.

⑤ More of this, less of that

These mountaineers are climbing Mount Everest. Mount Everest is approximately 8882 metres tall and is the highest mountain in the world. Even though the height is less than 9 kilometres, it takes several days to climb. Why do you think it takes so long to climb? Do you think it is easier to climb down a mountain than to climb up it?

 Look at the following statements and then explain briefly why they are true.

1. The steeper the mountain that you climb, the slower you will go.
2. The colder it is, the longer it will take for ice to melt.
3. The warmer it is, the less clothing you will need.
4. The faster the flow from a tap, the shorter the time it will take to fill a bath.
5. The bigger a price reduction, the lower the new cost will be.
6. The more you use a ball point pen, the shorter the time it will last.

 Callum and his friends each have savings accounts. Work out how much they will have in their accounts after paying in some cash.

1. Callum has £40 in his account. He pays in £27.
2. Winston has £62 in his account. He pays in £27.
3. Angie has £48 in her account. She pays in £25.
4. Jason is overdrawn by £35. He pays in £20.
5. Debbie is overdrawn by £45. She pays in £27.
6. Complete these sentences explaining how paying in money affects a balance.
   a. The more you pay into an account, the _____ the balance increases.
   b. The more you pay into an overdrawn account, the _____ the overdraft becomes.

Complete these sums.

1 ⊚ − 5 = 25
2 ⊚ − 10 = 37
3 ⊚ × 3 = 24
4 ⊚ +12 = 5
5 ⊚ + 10 = 4
6 ⊚ × 6 = 30

Nazmin and her friends played Crazy Golf. They each completed the course of ten holes. The score on each hole is how many times they hit the ball before it goes into the hole. Work out each player's total score.

1

Crazy Golf	
Nazmin	Score
Hole 1	6
Hole 2	4
Hole 3	8
Hole 4	2
Hole 5	5
Hole 6	7
Hole 7	3
Hole 8	6
Hole 9	2
Hole 10	4

2

Crazy Golf	
Gary	Score
Hole 1	7
Hole 2	5
Hole 3	4
Hole 4	7
Hole 5	6
Hole 6	6
Hole 7	3
Hole 8	5
Hole 9	4
Hole 10	2

3

Crazy Golf	
Tim	Score
Hole 1	4
Hole 2	5
Hole 3	4
Hole 4	3
Hole 5	1
Hole 6	6
Hole 7	5
Hole 8	4
Hole 9	2
Hole 10	3

4

Crazy Golf	
Sandra	Score
Hole 1	6
Hole 2	5
Hole 3	6
Hole 4	8
Hole 5	7
Hole 6	8
Hole 7	6
Hole 8	7
Hole 9	6
Hole 10	7

5 Who was the winner? Who came 2nd, 3rd and 4th?
6 Write a sentence to explain why the winner is the player with the lowest score.

Some tasks are easier with more than one person involved. For other tasks, it doesn't help. Look at the following tasks, and then write down whether it is helpful to have several people involved or not.

1 Decorating all of the rooms in a house
2 Clearing all the chairs away after a big concert
3 Making a telephone call
4 Boiling a kettle
5 Clearing a big garden that is overgrown with weeds
6 Write a sentence to explain why sometimes it is helpful to have a lot of people involved in a task and other times it is not.

Now look back at your work in this lesson.
• Think of some situations where the more you do of one thing, the less there is of something else.
• What did you find most interesting in this lesson?

⑥ One in four, one quarter

Stray or lost dogs are kept at the Battersea Dog's Home.
Sometimes the owners of the dogs find them here, and sometimes a new home is found for them.

In one week, 24 new dogs were brought into the Home.

1 By the end of the week, one in four of these dogs were taken back by their owners. What fraction of the dogs were taken back?

2 How many of the dogs were taken back?

3 Eight of the 24 dogs found new owners. What fraction of the dogs is this?

Sarah does a survey to find out the most popular pets in her class.
There are 36 pupils in her class. Sarah wrote down her results as fractions. How many pupils chose each pet?

1 ⅙ of the class have a rabbit.

2 ⅓ of them have a cat.

3 ¹⁄₁₂ of them have a snake.

4 ⅑ of them have a hamster.

5 ½ of them have a dog.

6 ¹⁄₁₈ of them have a tortoise.

Write down the answers to the following questions.

1 ⅕ of 30 = ✳

4 ⅔ of 24 = ✳

2 ⅛ of 24 = ✳

5 ⅙ of 42 = ✳

3 ⅓ of 24 = ✳

6 ⅑ of 27 = ✳

Wayne and his friends do part-time jobs. Work out how much each of them earns per hour.

1. Wayne works for four hours and earns £12.
2. Debbie works for six hours and earns £24.
3. Rachid works for four hours and earns £14.
4. Paul works for five hours and earns £25.
5. Jenny works for seven hours and earns £28.
6. Simon works for eight hours and earns £44.

Andy's class are going on a school journey. The total distance is 48 miles. Write down the answers to the following questions.

1. They travel four miles. What fraction of their journey is this?
2. They travel six miles. What fraction of their journey is this?
3. They travel eight miles. What fraction of their journey is this?
4. They travel 12 miles. What fraction of their journey is this?
5. They travel 16 miles. What fraction of their journey is this?
6. They travel 24 miles. What fraction of their journey is this?

Count up the total number of buttons and then answer these questions.

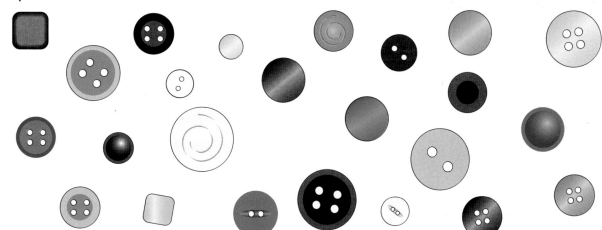

1. What fraction of the buttons are white?
2. What fraction of the buttons are yellow?
3. What fraction of the buttons are green?
4. What fraction of the buttons are red?
5. What fraction of the buttons are blue?
6. What fraction of the buttons are black?

Now look back at your work in this lesson.
- Write a sentence explaining how to find a fraction of a number, such as ⅕ of 60.
- Can you work out a fraction such as ¼ of 10? Explain your method.

Module F4

Shape and space

1 **3D drawings (1)**
Understanding 3D drawings of cubes or cuboids

2 **Enlargement**
Recognising when a shape has been enlarged and finding out how to enlarge a shape of your own

3 **3D drawings (2)**
Learning to build up 3D drawings

4 **Area of rectangles**
Finding the area of a surface that does not have squares

5 **Understanding volume**
Finding out how many centimetre cubes would fit in a box

6 **Area of a triangle**
Working out the area of right-angled triangles

Key words and phrases

3D drawing
cuboid
isometric paper
parallelogram
perpendicular
rhombus
vertical

cube
double the length of a side
enlargement
formula
outline of a rectangle
rectangle
rectangular block
stretching
vertical and horizontal lines

diagonal line
identical triangles
layers of unit cubes
right angle
volume of a box

1 3D drawings (1)

Some buildings look like building blocks. You can draw them using isometric paper.
In real life the lines are at right angles to each other. But on the page they look different. Why do you think that happens?

 Look at these drawings.

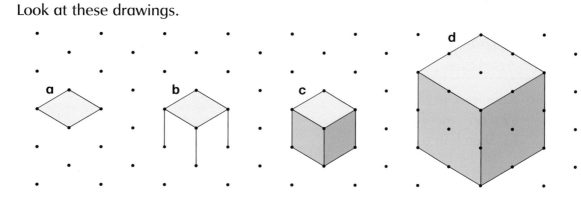

1 Using isometric paper, copy the diamond (rhombus) in the top left corner of your page, as in diagram **a**.

2 Now add a 1 cm line from each of the three points, as in diagram **b**.

3 Join the dots at the bottom of the shape to form a cube (see diagram **c**).

4 Carefully shade the side faces, leaving the top face white.

5 Now copy the diamond in diagram **d**. The sides are all 2 cm long. Follow the instructions you used for the 1 cm cube, but this time draw the lines 2 cm long. Shade the cube as before.

6 Repeat this process to draw cubes that have sides 3 cm, 4 cm, and 6 cm long.

 Now copy these shapes.

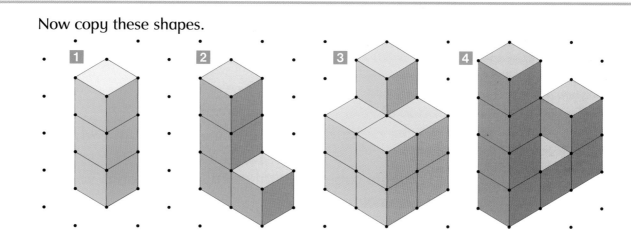

C

The drawings shown below are the same shapes as in exercise B, but they are shown in a different position.

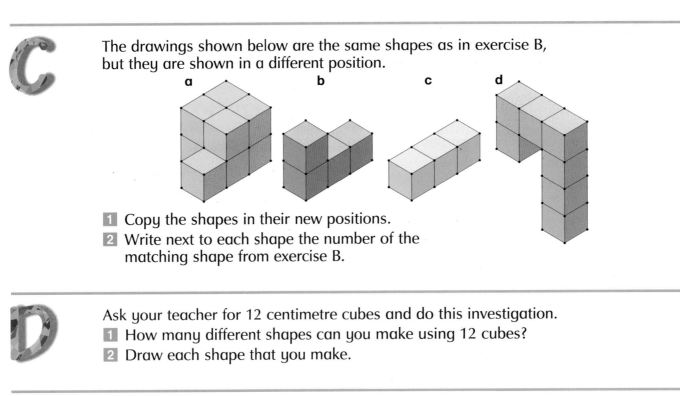

1 Copy the shapes in their new positions.
2 Write next to each shape the number of the matching shape from exercise B.

D

Ask your teacher for 12 centimetre cubes and do this investigation.
1 How many different shapes can you make using 12 cubes?
2 Draw each shape that you make.

E

Now look at these shapes.
1 Copy them in pencil.
2 Sketch in a cube to each of the positions marked with a dot.
3 Rub out any lines that you wouldn't be able to see if they were real 3D shapes.

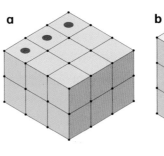  

Add three cubes   Add one cube   Add two cubes

F

Here are some more shapes.
1 Imagine that each cube marked with dots is removed. Draw the shapes after you have taken away the cubes marked with dots.

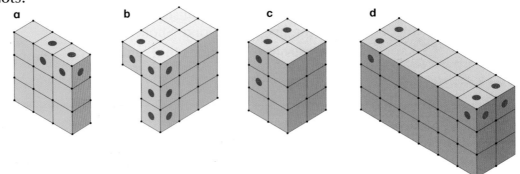

Now look back at your work in this lesson.
• What are the advantages of using isometric paper when sketching 3D shapes?
• How do real-life cubes look different from the ones you have drawn on isometric paper?

② Enlargement

You can enlarge or reduce the size of pictures as much as you wish. It is easy to see which picture is an enlargement of which. In this collection of pictures, which one has no enlargement?

A Look at these pictures of radios labelled **a** to **d**.

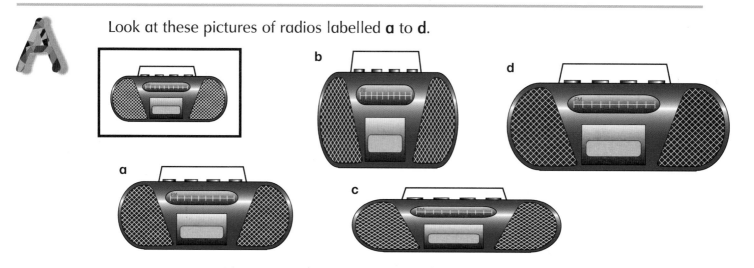

1 Which two radios are enlargements of the radio in the box?

The fish in the box is an enlargement of some of the fish labelled **a** to **d**.

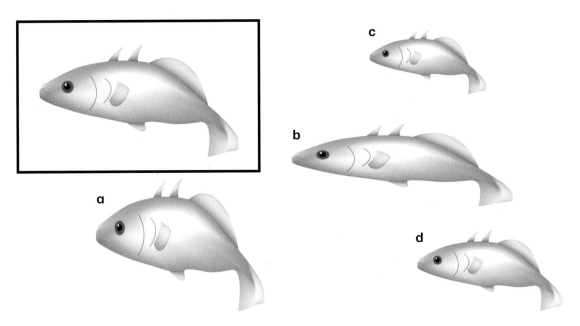

1 Write down the letters of the fish that have been enlarged.

Look at these squares and rectangles labelled **a** to **f**.

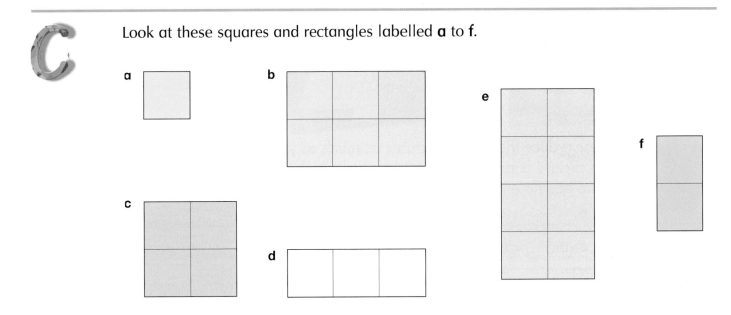

1 Find two pairs that show one shape as an enlargement of another.

2 Copy these pairs and label them.

3 Now write a sentence to say why the two odd shapes do not show enlargement.

4 On squared paper, draw a shape of your own.

5 Now draw the shape again at double the size. Make sure each of the sides is double the length of the sides in the original shape.

Shapes **b** and **c** are
enlargements of
shape **a**.

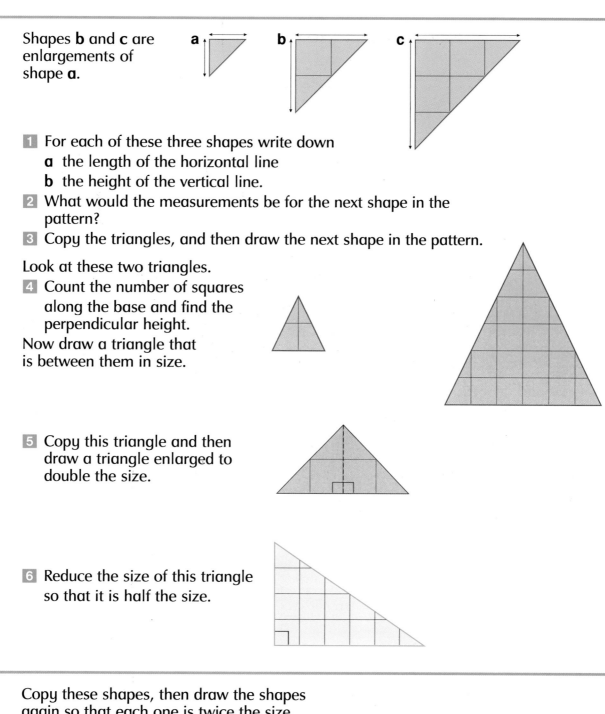

1 For each of these three shapes write down
  a the length of the horizontal line
  b the height of the vertical line.
2 What would the measurements be for the next shape in the
   pattern?
3 Copy the triangles, and then draw the next shape in the pattern.

Look at these two triangles.
4 Count the number of squares
   along the base and find the
   perpendicular height.
Now draw a triangle that
is between them in size.

5 Copy this triangle and then
   draw a triangle enlarged to
   double the size.

6 Reduce the size of this triangle
   so that it is half the size.

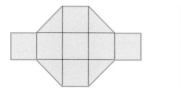

Copy these shapes, then draw the shapes
again so that each one is twice the size.

Now look back at your work in this lesson.
  • Think of ways that enlargement is useful.
  • When you are checking if one triangle is an enlargement of
    another, how many sides must you compare?

③ 3D drawings (2)

Some people can build very complicated and interesting shapes from small bricks like LEGO. Most people can also imagine the kind of shapes that combine to produce bigger shapes.
What scale models have you built?

A Look at these 2 cm × 2 cm × 2 cm cubes.

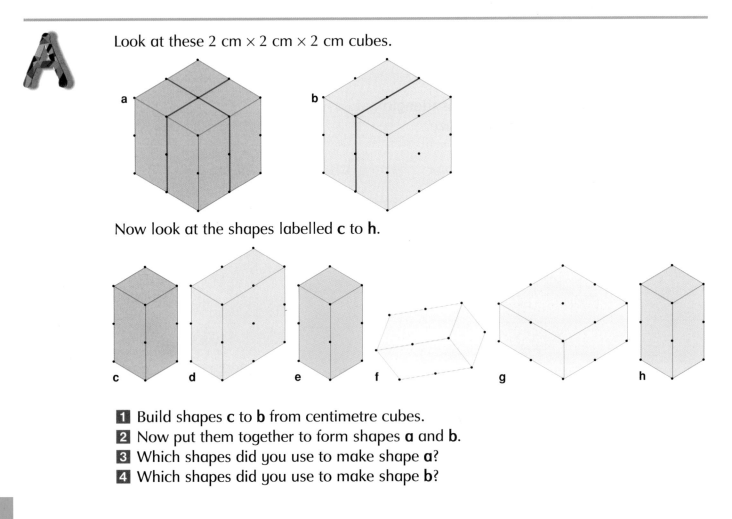

Now look at the shapes labelled **c** to **h**.

1 Build shapes **c** to **b** from centimetre cubes.
2 Now put them together to form shapes **a** and **b**.
3 Which shapes did you use to make shape **a**?
4 Which shapes did you use to make shape **b**?

B

Shapes 1, 2 and 3 have been sliced in half. The parts have become muddled up. For each shape find the pieces labelled **a** to **f** that fit together to form them.

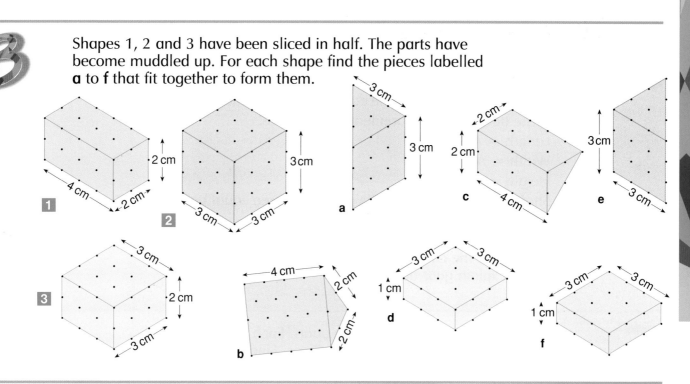

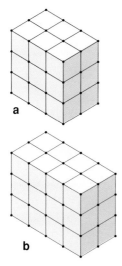

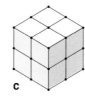

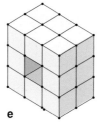

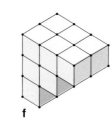

C

1 On isometric paper, draw three cubes that measure 4 cm × 4 cm × 4 cm.

Now draw line to show how you could cut these cubes in half in the following ways.
2 horizontally
3 vertically
4 diagonally
5 Draw the new shapes you have made.

D

Look at these shapes.

1 Which of the lettered shapes can be joined together to make shape **a** and shape **b**?
2 Find another way of splitting shapes **a** and **b** and draw your results.

E

You will need 27 centimetre cubes.

1. Make these cubes into one larger solid cube. You must not leave any gaps and you must use all the cubes.
2. Make a 3D drawing of the cube you have made.
3. Write down the measurements of the cube.

   Length = ☆ cm

   Width = ☆ cm

   Height = ☆ cm
4. Show how you can split this cube into three equal parts of the same shape.
5. Draw the shapes you have made.
6. Try to split the cube into two parts. Will both parts be equal sizes? Explain your answer.

F

Shapes 1, 2 and 3 have been taken apart. Each of the shapes is now in two, three or four smaller pieces. Find the shapes that go together to make the cube or cuboids.

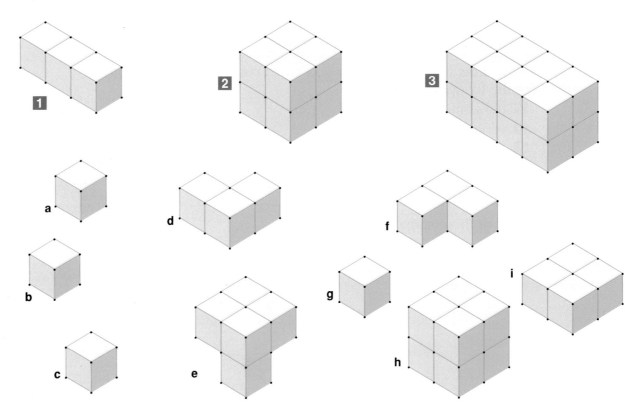

Now look back at your work in this lesson.
- Can you imagine how a block can be split into two or more smaller regular blocks?
- Can you build two different rectangular blocks made up of 12 cubic centimetres?

④ Area of a rectangle

This is one way of covering your walls! You could estimate the overall size of this wall by adding together the areas of all the posters.

 How many squares are there in each of these shapes? The first one has been done for you. Write your answers in the same way.

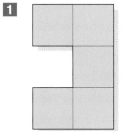

1

Five centimetre squares

2

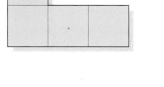

3

4

5

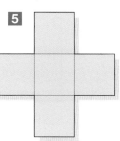

6

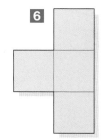

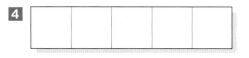 **7** Find the total number of squares that have been used to make these shapes.

8 On paper with centimetre squares draw two rectangles using all of the squares.

9 How many different rectangles can you make with the all the squares?

B

1. Copy the shapes from exercise A on to squared paper.
2. Carefully cut the shapes out.
3. Now try to fit them together so that they completely cover one of the rectangles you have drawn, without any spaces, and with no squares outside the edge of the rectangle.
4. When you are happy with your design, stick it on to the correct rectangle.

C

Four different colour rectangle cards are placed on top of each other as shown here.

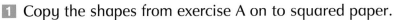

1. Which colour rectangle must be on top?
2. Which colour rectangle is at the bottom of the pile?
3. Find the area of each of these pieces of coloured card.

You cannot see all the squares to count how many cover the surface area, so find the length and width of the sides you can see. You can work out the area using this equation:

> area = height × width

4. Record your results in a table.

Colour	Height (cm)	Width (cm)	Area (cm sq)
green	8 cm	× 14 cm	= 112 cm sq
blue	✳	× ✳	= ✳
yellow	✳	× ✳	= ✳
red	✳	× ✳	= ✳

D

James wants to cover one wall of his bedroom with the posters of bikes. He measures the width and height of his wall. The width is 3 metres and the height is 2.5 metres.

1 Work out the measurements of the wall in centimetres. (remember 1 m = 100 cm)

2 Find the area of the wall in centimetres squared. You may like to use a calculator.

James measures his posters. The measurements of the posters are in the table below.

Poster number	Width (cm)	Height (cm)	Area (cm sq)
1	100	60	6000 cm sq
2	120	60	
3	80	60	
4	70	120	
5	100	120	
6	70	70	
7	130	90	
8	70	100	
9	60	100	
10	100	70	

3 Copy the table and use a calculator to find the area of each poster and fill in your results in the table.

4 Add these values to find the total area of the posters.

5 What do you notice about the area of the wall compared with the total area of the posters?

E

1 Using a piece of A3 paper, draw a rectangle 30 cm wide by 25 cm high. This is a scale drawing of Jason's wall.

2 On squared paper, draw the outlines of Jason's ten posters. Use a scale of 1 cm on your drawing to represent 10 cm in real life. So a poster that really measures 100 cm wide × 60 cm high would be 10 cm wide and 6 cm high in your drawing.

3 Draw a little picture on each one so you remember which way up they go.

4 Carefully cut out the posters and try different arrangements to fit all of them on your drawing of the wall.

5 When you are happy that the posters are all in the correct positions, stick down your design.

Now look back at your work in this lesson
- What measurements do you need to find the area of any rectangle?
- If you can put two rectangles together to make a bigger rectangle, what do the two rectangles have in common?

⑤ **Understanding volume**

Which of these boxes has the biggest volume?
What do you need to know to calculate the volume of a box?

1. Using 12 interlocking centimetre cubes, investigate how many different cuboids you can make.
2. It may help you to work out the different ways you can multiply three numbers to make 12. For example, $6 \times 2 \times 1 = 12$.
3. Draw your results on isometric paper.
4. Write the measurements of the cuboids along the sides.
5. Record your results in a table.

Length	Width	Height	Volume
6 cm	× 2 cm	× 1 cm	= 12 cm cube

This shape can be made from centimetre cubes.

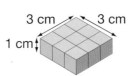

1. How many cubes make up the shape?
2. Each cube has a volume of 1 cm cubed. What is the volume of the shape?

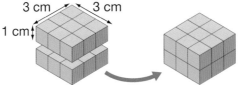

3. If we add another layer, how many cubes are there altogether? An easy way of working out the volume, instead of counting the cubes, is to multiply the length of the shape by its width, and then multiply by the number of layers.

> length × width × height = volume

4. Use the equation to work out the volume of the cuboid.
5. If there was another layer, what would be the total volume of the cuboid?
6. How many cubes would you have if there were five 3 cm × 3 cm layers?

C

Find out how many centimetre cubes it takes to build these cuboids.

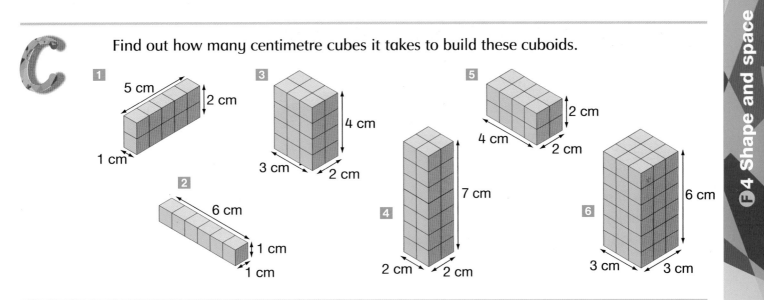

1 5 cm, 2 cm, 1 cm

2 6 cm, 1 cm, 1 cm

3 4 cm, 3 cm, 2 cm

4 7 cm, 2 cm, 2 cm

5 4 cm, 2 cm, 2 cm

6 6 cm, 3 cm, 3 cm

D

1 Work out the volume of each of these cuboids labelled **a** to **f**.

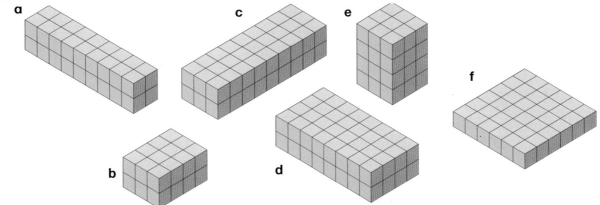

a   c   e   f   b   d

2 Which of the cuboids is made from exactly 36 centimetre cubes?

3 Which of the cuboids is made from fewer than 36 cubes?

4 Which of the cuboids is made from more than 36 cubes?

5 Can you think of any other cuboids made from exactly 36 centimetre cubes?

E

Use the length, width and height of these cuboids and find their volumes. You may use a calculator to work out your answers.

1 A cereal box measuring 20 cm × 5 cm × 15 cm

2 A chocolate box measuring 16 cm × 12 cm × 6 cm

3 A calculator box measuring 12 cm × 8 cm × 2 cm

4 A roller blade box measuring 45 cm × 36 cm × 12 cm

> Now look back at your work in this lesson.
> * What measurements do you need to calculate the volume of a cuboid?
> * Can you explain how the formula for the volume of a cuboid works?

⑥ Area of a triangle

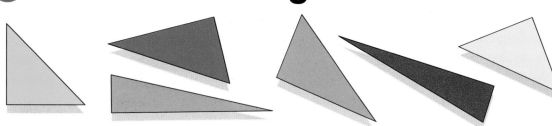

What does it mean when someone says two identical right-angle triangles make up a rectangle?

Work through these exercises about triangles.

1 Using squared paper, draw a 4 cm × 4 cm square.

2 What is the area of the square?

3 Draw a vertical line to split the square in half.

4 What shapes have you made?

5 What is the area of each rectangle?

6 Now draw another 4 cm × 4 cm square. This time, draw a line to cut the square in half diagonally.

7 Carefully cut out the square and then cut along the diagonal line.

8 Mark the right angle with a cross on each of your triangles.

9 Can you prove that both shapes are of equal size?

10 Count the whole squares first, then the parts of squares. What is the area of each triangle in cm sq?

11 What do you notice about the answers to question 5 and question 10?

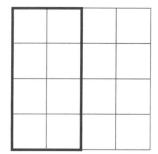

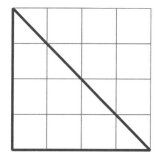

1 Draw this rectangle and mark the diagonal line to split the rectangle in half.

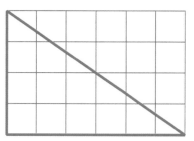

2 Mark the right angles with a cross.

3 Find the area of each triangle. Count the whole squares first, putting a dot on each whole square.
Now count the parts of squares. Write your answer.

4 What is the height of the triangle, from the corner marked with a cross to one corner?

5 What is the length of the triangle, from the corner marked with a cross to the other corner?

C

> If you multiply the length by the height to find the area of
> the whole rectangle, and then take half of the answer, you
> will have the area of the triangle.

1 Work out the areas of the rectangles labelled **a** to **c**.

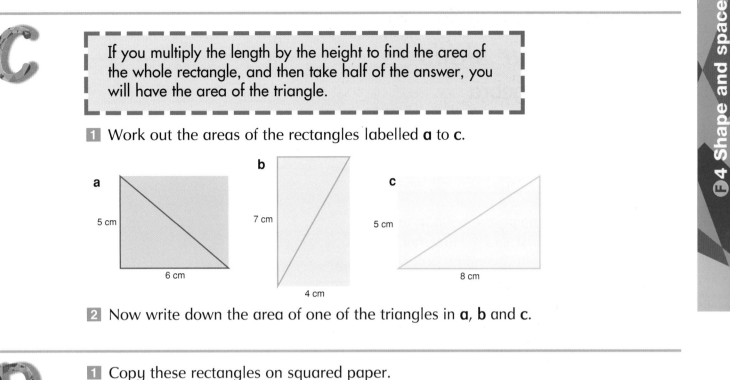

a 5 cm, 6 cm

b 7 cm, 4 cm

c 5 cm, 8 cm

2 Now write down the area of one of the triangles in **a**, **b** and **c**.

D

1 Copy these rectangles on squared paper.

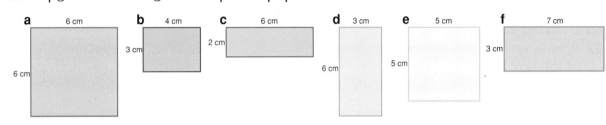

a 6 cm, 6 cm   **b** 4 cm, 3 cm   **c** 6 cm, 2 cm   **d** 3 cm, 6 cm   **e** 5 cm, 5 cm   **f** 7 cm, 3 cm

2 Now draw in a diagonal line on each drawing to split the
   rectangle in half.

3 Find the area of the triangles you have formed. Remember
   to mark the right angles of your triangles with a cross.

4 Does the direction that you draw the diagonal make any
   difference to the area of the triangles?

E

1 Find the area of the triangles
   labelled **a**, **b** and **c**.

2 Fill in the missing
   measurements for
   b and **c**.

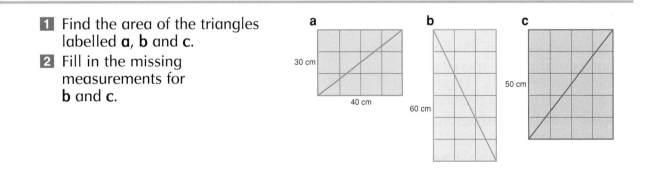

a 30 cm, 40 cm   **b** 60 cm   **c** 50 cm

> Now look back at your work in this lesson.
> * What measurements do you need to calculate the area of a
>   right-angle triangle?
> * When you cut a rectangle in half with a diagonal what can you
>   say about the two triangles?

Module Ⓕ1–Ⓕ4

Review your skills

Number and algebra

0 ————————————————— 10

1 If A = 5 and B = 9, mark A and B on the line.

50 ————————————————— 100

2 Mark on the line the position of 65p and 80p.
3 Ten cans of cola cost £3.70. How much does one can cost?
4 Put these numbers in ascending order: 3.54, 3.48, 4.02, 4.52

Here are the finishing times of pupils in a race.

Paul	8.93 seconds
Fiona	9.02 seconds
Sayeed	8.64 seconds
Rushna	9.54 seconds

5 Who won the race?
6 a What is ¾ – ½ ?   **b** What is 2 – ¾ ?
7 Rose is given a full box of chocolates. She eats ¼ of them. What fraction of the box is left?
8 In Curtley's group of seven pupils, three have cable television. What fraction of the group is this?
9 Which is greater?   **a** ¼ or 80%   **b** ½ or 45%?
10 What percentage of an hour is 45 minutes?

Handling data

Write down the value of the five numbers that the arrows are pointing to on the horizontal line.

Joe felt ill on Monday. His father plotted his temperature each morning and evening on this graph. He gave him medicine on Tuesday evening.

6 What was Joe's temperature on Tuesday evening?
7 By how much did his temperature rise from Monday evening?
8 What was Joe's highest temperature in the week?
9 How does this graph show when Joe was getting better?
10 Was the lowest temperature at the start or at the end of the week?

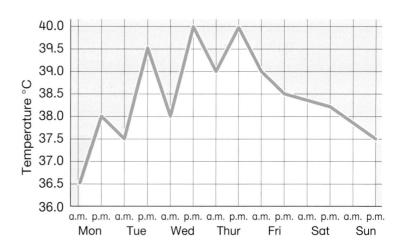

Number and algebra

1 I buy a melon for 42p and a loaf of bread for 37p. How much change should I get from £1?

2 What is the value of 12 50p coins?

3 Mandy watches four half-hour television programmes. Then she spends 25 minutes on the phone to her friend. How much time is this altogether?

4 Rushna buys 33 sweets at 3p each. How much does this cost her?

5 There are 40 boxes which each contain six video tapes. How many video tapes are there altogether?

6 There are 30 pupils in Winston's class. One fifth of them have cable television. How many is this?

7 It takes Sandra 15 minutes to walk to the station and her train journey takes 38 minutes. How much time is this altogether?

8 Geoff buys three videos at £14 each. He also pays £2.10 in postage and packaging. How much does he pay altogether?

9 There are 33 pupils in Wayne's class. Eleven of them go to a pop concert. What fraction of the class is this?

10 Andy spends 55 minutes every day in football training. How long does he spend training in a week?

Shape and space

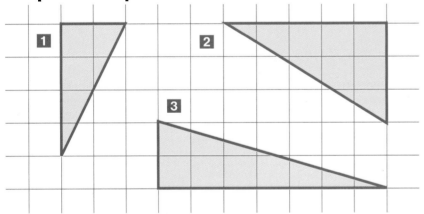

Find the area of each triangle in square units.

4 What would the area of a rectangle with sides of 5 and 12 units be?

5 Enlarge triangle 1 by a factor of 2 (doubling the sides).

Now try this...

Imagine you have five cubes of one unit, like the one shown.

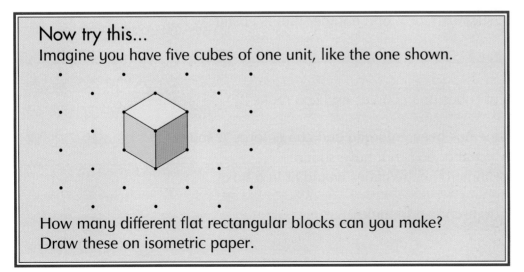

How many different flat rectangular blocks can you make?
Draw these on isometric paper.

Check your skills

You can check how well you can do the things listed here. Get your parents and friends to help.

Number and algebra

1 I can read scales by estimating to one decimal place between numbered marks, and can imagine where the marks are shown.

2 I can solve problems where I use multiplication or division of a whole number by 100 or by 1000.

3 I can compare decimal numbers with one or two decimal places, and know when a number with three digits can be less than a number with two digits.

4 I can add and subtract numbers with halves and quarters. I can say what fraction something is out of a whole.

5 I know and can use percentages from 0% to 100%. I can link them to fractions and understand their meanings.

Handling data

1 I can use a coding system with two symbols to find or store data.

2 I can use graphs or tables which show money or temperature in different scales.

3 I can plot data with one decimal place in graphs.

4 I can read graphs of time and distance.

5 I can use data intervals to group large amounts of data when working with histograms.

Number and algebra

1 I can solve problems which involve addition or subtraction without the use of a calculator.

2 I can solve problems which involve multiplication by a single-digit number, without using a calculator, and find the easiest way to do so.

3 I can solve problems which require the use of two operations, such as addition and subtraction or addition and multiplication, by a whole number.

4 I can understand relationships of the type 'the more of this the less of that'.

5 I can find a single fraction, such as $\frac{1}{3}$ or $\frac{1}{2}$ of a number that is easily divisible.

Shape and space

1 I understand 3D drawings of cubes and cuboids and can make 3D drawings of objects.

2 I can recognise when a shape has been enlarged and can enlarge a shape.

3 I can find the area of a surface that does not have squares.

4 I can find out how many centimetre/metre cubes would fit in a box, by using numbers.

5 I can work out the area of right-angled triangles.

Number and algebra

❶ Time units

Working with different units of time to solve problems where there is a mixture of units. Converting from one unit to another

❷ Departures and arrivals

Using departure and arrival times in a timetable

❸ The larger the unit...

Knowing what happens to a numerical value of measurement if a larger or smaller unit is used

❹ How accurate?

Estimating the accuracy of measurements in everyday situations. Deciding what level of accuracy is required in a situation

❺ Temperature ranges

Knowing the range of temperatures likely on a certain day using degrees Celsius or degrees Fahrenheit

❻ Measurement skills

Reviewing and practising measurement skills

Key words and phrases

arrival
arrive
day
delayed
depart
departure
early
half hour
hours
late
minutes
on time
seconds
week

accuracy
approximate
centimetres
estimate
feet
gallons
inches
kilograms
limit
litres
metres
pints
pounds
stones
within
yards

degrees Celsius
degrees Fahrenheit
temperature

① Time units

In science fiction films, people can go backwards and forwards in time. If they want to arrive at an event in history, they need to set their time machines to the exact moment of the event. That means calculating the time in years, days, hours, minutes and seconds. One mistake and they could be late.

Have you ever been late because you made a mistake over the time?

A

1 Change 2½ hours into minutes.
2 A train journey takes 33 hours. If the train leaves at 2:30 p.m., when does it arrive at its destination?
3 How many days of holiday do you have if your last day at work is Friday May 7th and your first day back at work is Monday May 24th?
4 How many minutes are there in 11 hours?
5 How many seconds are there in 11 hours?

B

All the pupils in Hasan's class have completed a time management survey as part of their work on study skills. Hasan worked out that he spent 2½ hours doing Maths homework each week.

1 Which of the pupils spent longer than Hasan doing Maths homework?

Name	Time
Mary	90 mins
Joe	2 hrs 10 mins
Naomi	2 hrs 40 mins
Jacob	140 mins
Susan	160 mins
Sam	2 hrs 35 mins

C

In the survey, each pupil put down the time spent sleeping.

Name	Fall asleep at	Time spent asleep	Wake up at
Mary	10:00 p.m.	8 hrs	6:00 a.m.
Joe	9:30 p.m.	9 hrs	★
Naomi	10:15 p.m.	10 hrs	★
Jacob	10:10 p.m.	9 hrs 20 mins	★
Susan	9:45 p.m.	9½ hrs	★
Sam	10:30 p.m.	8 hrs 15 mins	★

1 Copy this table and fill in the time that each pupil wakes up.

D

Last day at school	First day back at school	Length of holiday
22 October	1 November	1 week 2 days
21 December	6 January	
18 February	28 February	
14 April	2 May	
26 May	5 June	

Copy this table.

1 Work out how long each of these school holidays lasts and write your answers in the table.
   Give your answers in weeks and days. The first one is done for you.

E

Write down the answers to these questions.

1 What is the exact time now?
   What will the time be 131 hours from now?

2 Alice held her breath for 69 seconds. Maria held her breath for 1 minute 10 seconds. Who held their breath the longest?

3 Ruth likes her eggs boiled for 3½ minutes. For how many seconds should Ruth set the kitchen timer?

4 Hannah learnt her lines for a play 75 hours after being given the script. Vic had learnt her lines in 3 days and 6 hours. Who was quicker to learn their lines?

5 Harry plans to spend the whole of Saturday watching videos without a break. Which film will he be watching after eight hours, if he watches them in this order?

Die Hard II	2 hrs 5 mins
Possums	1 hr 50 mins
Deadly Invasion	1 hr 35 mins
Dangerous Minds	1 hr 55 mins
Sunset Beat	1 hr 45 mins
Spinal Tap	1 hr 50 mins

F

You may use a calculator to help you answer these questions.

1 How many days are there in a week?
2 How many hours are there in a week?
3 How many minutes are there in a week?
4 How many seconds are there in a week?
5 There are 365 days in a year. How many hours is that?
6 How many minutes are there in a year?
7 How many seconds are there in a year?

Now look back at your work in this lesson.
- How do you convert from one unit of time to another?
- How do you work out how long things take when they are measured in a mixture of units?

② Departures and arrivals

When there's only one train a week, people will do anything to get on board!
Do you live in an area where the trains and buses are rare? Do you think that is the main reason why so many people still travel by car?

Look at the timetable below and answer these questions.

Cambridge Depart	London Kings Cross Arrive	Cambridge Depart	London Kings Cross Arrive
06:45	07:43	10:27	11:28
07:15	08:13	10:45	11:38
07:45	08:43	11:15	12:06
08:15	09:13	11:27	12:28
08:21	09:42	11:45	12:37
08:45	09.43	12:15	13:06
09:15	10:06	12:27	13:28
09:27	10:28	12:45	13:37
09:45	10:37	13:15	14:06
10:15	11:06	13:27	14:28

1 What time does the 09:15 train from Cambridge arrive at King's Cross?
2 How long does this journey take?
3 If the train was running 20 minutes late, what time would it depart?
4 If the train was delayed for *another* 15 minutes, what time would the train arrive at King's Cross?

B

Diana arrives at Cambridge station to travel to King's Cross at the times shown below. Look at the timetable and decide which train should she catch on each of these days.

1. Monday 8:40 a.m.
2. Tuesday 10:30 a.m.
3. Wednesday 9:17 a.m.
4. Thursday 7:30 a.m.
5. Friday 8:10 a.m.

What is the latest time she arrives at King's Cross station?

C

Ravi also travels from Cambridge to London each day. He must get to London by the times shown below. What is the latest train that he could catch each day to avoid arriving late?

1. Monday 10:40 a.m.
2. Tuesday 9:30 a.m.
3. Wednesday 11:15 a.m.
4. Thursday 8:30 a.m.
5. Friday 1:20 p.m.

D

Look at the trains leaving Cambridge between 8:00 a.m. and 11:00 a.m.

1. How many trains leave for King's Cross in this interval?
2. How long does the fastest train take?
3. How many of these fast trains are there?
4. How long did the slowest train take?
5. How many of these slow trains are there?

E

All the trains from Cambridge to London leaving between 8:00 a.m. and 10:00 a.m. are cancelled because of an accident. The trains start to run again after 10:00 a.m. but they are all leaving half an hour late.

1. What time does the first train leave after 10:00 a.m.?
2. The journeys are taking 15 minutes longer than normal. What time does this train arrive in King's Cross?
3. What time train should you catch if you want to get to London for 12:00 a.m.?

Now look back at your work in this lesson.
- How do you calculate the length of journeys from a timetable?
- How do choose the right train to arrive at a certain time?

③ The larger the unit...

This horse measures about 15 hands from its hooves to its back. The girl is about five feet tall.
Which measurment units are bigger – hands or feet?

1. Laura and Katie measure how wide a textbook is using finger widths. The book is 14 of Laura's finger widths and 12 of Katie's finger widths. Who has the widest fingers?
2. They measure their desk in inches and then in feet. They write down 3 and 36, but forget to put the units. Which measurement is in feet and which is in inches?
3. Katie weighs 7 stones. Laura weighs 90 pounds. They know that there are 14 pounds in a stone. Which unit is bigger?
4. What is Katy's weight in pounds?
5. What is Laura's weight in stones and pounds?

Sam and Heather are designing a play cabin for their garden. They mark the shape out on the ground and then measure it.

1. Sam measures the width to be 120 and Heather makes it 48. Who is using inches and who is using centimetres?
2. They agree to use metric lengths for the length. Sam gets 195, Heather's measurement is just less than 2. Why do you think this has happened?
3. The roof needs to be high enough for them to stand up. They mark this height against an old wall and measure it. Sam says it will be 8 planks high. Heather has written 12 hand spans. Which is wider, a plank or a hand span?
4. The doorway is marked on the floor and they both measure it in footsteps. Sam has bigger feet than Heather. Who will write down fewer footsteps?

C

1. Emily knows that there are 8 pints in a gallon. If it takes 40 pints of water to fill the pond, will this be $40 \times 8 = 320$ gallons or $40 \div 8 = 5$ gallons?

2. She knows there are 100 cm in a metre. The pond should be 250 cm wide. How many metres is that?

3. The depth is 800 millimetres. Sarah tells her there are 10 mm in a centimetre. Should she multiply or divide by 10 to find the depth in centimetres?

4. The length of the pond is marked on the ground. Sarah measures it to be 2.5 and Emily measures 2.7. Who is using yards and who is using metres?

> 1 yard = 36 inches, 1 metre = 39 inches

D

One kilogram is approximately the same as two pounds. These animals are lined up in order of weight with the heaviest first.

1. For each animal, decide whether the units should be kilograms or pounds.

E

Each of these measurements is given in two different units. Use your common sense and what you have learned this lesson to decide what units each measurement must be.

Object	Measurement	First unit	Second unit
Door	height	6	180
Man	weight	70	11
Pencil	length	15	6
Watering can	capacity	2	10

Now look back at your work in this lesson.
* How do you tell which of two units are used in a measurement?
* Have you found that a larger unit results in a smaller number being recorded?

④ How accurate?

When someone says he has caught a five-foot fish, we know that is most likely to be a bit longer or a bit shorter than that. Sometimes people don't need to give accurate measurements. Can you think of some examples of when you only give a rough number as a measurement?

A These pupils use measurements in their conversation.

1 Which of these groups is using more exact measurements?
2 In the first group, do you think that *1 mile* or *10 minutes* is more accurate?
3 In the second group, do you think that *three inches* or *six feet* is more accurate?

B Look at the sentences below. For each distance, decide whether it has been measured carefully. Explain your answers.

1 It is 150 miles from Cambridge to Leeds.
2 The inside lane around a running track is 400 m.
3 The carrot seeds were planted 10 cm below the soil.
4 We will need 50 m of rope to mark out the car park area for the school fête.
5 The space required for this kitchen unit is 600 mm.

C Here are some times. Decide which ones are measured carefully.

1. This egg has been boiled for 31 minutes.
2. It took me two hours to get home.
3. This video lasts for 40 minutes.
4. I can hold my breath for 65 seconds.
5. I am 14 years old.
6. For each sentence, write down an example of a more accurate time.

D Here are some answers in a questionnaire.

```
Age: 26 years
Height: 220 cm
Weight: 72 kg
22 hours of TV viewed last week
6 pints of beer drunk last week
3 miles walked last week
```

1. Which of these answers are exact values?
2. Within what range could each of these values lie?

E Use your knowledge about litres and pints to work out what is the smallest number of pints in these containers and what could be the largest number. (Remember, two pints of liquid are a little bit more than a litre.)

> 1. There's about 30 litres in that one. 3. There must be 5 litres in the third.
> 2. There's only a litre left in the second. 4. There's half a litre in the last one.

Now look back at your work in this lesson.
- How do you tell when accuracy is important in a measurement?
- How do you decide how much more or less accurate a measurement could be?

⑤ Temperature ranges

To break the world record for ice bathing this man needed to stay in the zero degrees water for longer than one hour and four minutes. He gave up after 36 minutes! What do you think zero degrees means?

The temperature at which water turns to ice is called its freezing point. We can write this in degrees Celsius as 0°C or in degrees Fahrenheit as 32°F.

1 Make a list of things you might do when the temperature is below freezing point.

2 On a hot day, the temperature might reach 30°C. We can write this in Fahrenheit as 86°F. Make a list of things you might do when the temperature is hot.

Look at this list of temperatures.

Now look at these pictures. Match each picture to one of the temperatures.

| 1 | 2 | 3 | 4 | 5 |

Match the same pictures from exercise B to the temperatures shown here in Fahrenheit.

D

1 Put these temperatures in order starting with the coldest.

0°C	30°F	18°C	50°F	20°C	–2°C

2 For each temperature, write down what sort of a day you think it would be.

3 Write down an activity you might do in each of these temperatures.

E

1 Copy these Fahrenheit and Celsius scales.

Fahrenheit

    20   30   40   50   60   70   80   90   100

–10   0   10   30   40

Celsius

2 Mark the temperatures from exercise B on the Celsius scale.

3 Mark the temperatures from exercise C on the Fahrenheit scale.

F

Here is the script for a weather forecaster to read.

The temperature this afternoon is about 40 °F. Overnight it will fall by up to 20 °F and there is a chance of snow.
Spain is enjoying much milder weather, with temperatures of around 60 °F set to rise by 10 °F by the end of the week.

Write down answers to the following questions in degrees Celsius.

1 What is the temperature this afternoon?

2 How much will the temperature fall during the night?

3 What will the temperature be tonight?

4 What will the temperature be in Spain at the end of the week?

> Now look back at your work in this lesson.
> - Estimate the temperature on a winter day using Fahrenheit and Celsius.
> - Estimate the temperature on a hot summer day.

⑥ Measurement skills

This weather balloon measures temperature, wind speed and humidity at different heights. Forecasters use several balloons in different places to predict the weather. The measurements in each balloon are very accurate. Why do you think weather forecasts are often approximate?

The pupils in Hasan's class did a time management survey as part of their work on study skills. Hasan worked out that he spent 3 hours 20 minutes eating with his family last week. The results from other students are given below.

Name	Time
Mary	190 mins
Joe	3½ hrs
Naomi	3 hrs 40 mins
Jacob	220 mins
Susan	200 mins
Sam	3 hrs 35 mins

1 Which of the pupils spent longer eating with their family than Hasan?

Here is a timetable showing trains from Cambridge to London.

David arrives at Cambridge station to travel to London at the following times.

Monday	7:30 a.m.
Tuesday	7:00 a.m.
Wednesday	8:20 a.m.
Thursday	9:30 a.m.
Friday	11:00 a.m.

1 Which train should he catch on each day?

Cambridge Depart	London Kings Cross Arrive	Cambridge Depart	London Kings Cross Arrive
06:45	07:43	09:45	10:37
07:15	08:13	10:15	11:06
07:45	08:43	10:27	11:28
08:15	09:13	10:45	11:38
08:21	09:42	11:15	12:06
08:45	09.43	11:27	12:28
09:15	10:06	11:45	12:37
09:27	10:28	12:15	13:06

Daniel, Callum and Ishbel use lots of ways to measure how far their dog Gemma has jumped. They mark the place she landed and each pupil measures the distance.

1. First they each stride out the length. Daniel measures eight paces, Callum measures nine paces and Ishbel measures ten paces. Who has the longest stride?

2. Then they each collect a stick and use it to find the distance. Daniel records 32 sticks lengths, Callum records 35 stick lengths and Ishbel records ten stick lengths. Whose sticks were similar in length? Who had the longest stick?

3. They each take a sheet out of the same newspaper and use it to measure the length of Gemma's jump. Daniel measures seven sheets, Callum measures eight sheets and Ishbel measures seven sheets. Why do you think these measurements are not all the same?

4. Which of these three ways – using strides, sticks or sheets of newspaper – is most reliable? Give a reason for your choice.

1. Choose six different objects in your classroom. Measure the width of some small items in finger widths, some medium items in hand spans and some longer lengths in paces. Write your measurements down.

2. Ask a friend to do the same for each item and write these measurements down.

3. Explain how you know from these measurements who had wider finger widths, wider hand spans and longer strides.

1. Find six measurements written in the text of a newspaper or magazine. For example, you might find the size of a crowd, a distance or a temperature.

2. Write down these measurements, remembering to say what each one is measuring.

3. For each measurement, say whether you think it is a large value or small value.

1. Write down in degrees Celsius the temperature of a day that is hot enough for sunbathing.

2. Would 2°C be cold enough for the roads to become icy?

3. Would you need to wear a coat if the temperature is 30°F?

4. Would you be too warm in a living room that was 35°C?

5. Would a snowman melt at a temperature of 1°C?

Now look back at your work in this lesson.
- Are there any parts in these exercises that you still find difficult?
- What types of measurement are you good at estimating?

Module F6

Handling data

① Mode

Finding and using the mode (the most popular, or most common value) in a set of data

② Range

Calculating and using the range of a set of data, explaining how it could affect the final result of a survey

③ Probability order

Sorting events according to the probability of them happening and placing them in order of how likely they are

④ Fairness

Choosing a method of selection that is fair and knowing when a method is unfair

⑤ Probability scale

Giving an estimate of the chance of an event happening, using a scale of 0 to 100% or 0 to 1

⑥ Probability and data

Using the skills developed in the previous five lessons

Key words and phrases

comparing words: larger, heavier, longer and difference

mode
most popular
frequent
most common
set of values
data

bias
certain
choose
even chance
evens
fair
likely
probability
share
unlikely

① **Mode**

Do you think that the market traders sell the same amount of fruit each week?
People *shop around* to find the best price for what they want, then look at the quality and size.
Do you think the price of fruit varies much between different shops?
What items cost the same wherever you buy them?

Find the mode of these prices which are being charged for vegetables in the market.

1 Cauliflower: | 40p 35p 55p 50p 40p 35p 45p 40p |

2 Cabbages: | 75p 65p 50p 60p 65p 70p 60p 65p |

3 Green beans (250 g): | 60p 55p 75p 60p 70p 55p 80p 55p |

Greg comes to the market twice a week to open his fruit stall.
He sells his oranges in different sized bags: large, medium and small.
On Monday he sells 44 large bags, 65 medium bags and 53 small bags.
On Thursday he sells 47 large bags, 52 medium bags and 38 small bags.

1 Organise the data into a table.
2 Which size bag do you think he should make the most of for the next week?

Jo sells T-shirts in the Market. These tables show how many T-shirts she sold in each size last Saturday.

Men's size	Quantity	Women's size	Quantity
38	10	32	25
40	8	34	14
42	25	36	37
44	15	38	22
46	4	40	10

1 Which was the most popular men's size?
2 What was the mode of the women's sizes?
3 When Jo orders her new supplies, which men's sizes would you expect her to order least of?

On Halim's shoe stall, the most popular size of ladies' shoe nearly every week is size 6. The most popular size for men is size 9.

1 Today was much the same as usual. He sold 48 pairs of ladies' shoes in size 5, 32 pairs in size 7, but fewer of the larger and smaller sizes. If size 6 was still the mode, what was the least number of this size that he could have sold?

2 Today, Halim sold 43 pairs of size 9 shoes. Here is part of his list of sales for men's shoes.

Size 5	8
Size 6	17
Size 7	29
Size 8	45
Size 9	43
Size 10	20
Size 11	13

3 Was size 9 the mode today?

The walls along the side of the market need a new coat of paint. All the traders are asked which colour they would prefer them to be. Here are the results of their vote.

Terracotta Green Blue White Blue Green
Blue Beige Terracotta Terracotta White Blue
White Blue White Blue Green White
Terracotta Green Terracotta Beige Blue
Blue White White Blue Terracotta Beige
Terracotta Blue Blue White Green Blue
Blue Beige Terracotta Blue Blue Green
Terracotta Green Blue White Green Terracotta
Terracotta Green Terracotta Blue Blue Blue

1 Make a tally chart in your book to show the result of the vote.
2 Find the mode from your table.
3 Write down which colour you think they will choose and a reason why.
4 If you have time to do the survey, write down your results in a useful way.
5 Can you think of any good uses for your results? Who may want to know the results, and how could they use them?

Now look back at your work in this lesson.
- When is it useful to find the mode of some numbers?
- If you have a lot of number data, what is the best way of finding the mode?

② Range

Athletes don't always perform at the same level. Why do you think they can throw further or run faster on some days?

Think of a running event that you have taken part in. What is your fastest time for that event? And your slowest time?

What is the *range* of your times?

Write down the answers to these questions about range.

Find the range of the following sets of numbers.

1 24, 23, 27, 34, 29, 27, 33, 28, 26, 32

2 65, 75, 69, 73, 68, 75, 66, 71, 68, 59, 64

3 45, 4, 110, 67, 23, 0

4 Which of these sets has the widest range?

5 Which has the narrowest range?

6 What calculation do you use to find the range of any set of data?

The range of Pam's swimming practice over four nights was seven lengths. She completed 25 lengths on Monday, 30 lengths on Tuesday and 28 lengths on Wednesday.

1 If 25 lengths was her shortest swim, how far did she swim on Thursday?

2 If 30 lengths was her longest swim, how far did she swim on Thursday?

Eddie is practising his golf. Here are the distances he drives over ten shots.

55 m	58 m	62 m	58 m	57 m	64 m	62 m	49 m	58 m	56 m

1 Find the range of these distances.

2 Here are the numbers of shots he takes for each of the 18 holes on the course.

4	5	3	4	2	6	3	4	2
7	5	4	6	5	8	4	5	6

What was the range of his scores?

D

In the first four matches of the season, Jack scored 22, 25, 28 and 16 runs. Rupesh scored 55, 14, 10 and 12 runs.

1 How many runs did Jack score altogether?
2 How many runs did Rupesh score altogether?
3 Find the range of Jack's scores.
4 Find the range of Rupesh's scores.
5 Which player would you choose to play in your team?
6 Explain why you chose him.

E

Mrs O'Connor drives from London to Norwich each weekend to visit her parents. She times herself over the journey for several weeks to find out if the traffic on the roads is getting worse as summer approaches. Here are her times for eight weeks.

2 hours 45 minutes	2 hours 30 minutes
2 hours 38 minutes	2 hours 57 minutes
2 hours 55 minutes	2 hours 49 minutes
2 hours 56 minutes	3 hours 10 minutes

1 What was the time of her fastest journey?
2 How long did the slowest journey take?
3 What was the range of the journey times?
4 Do you think that the roads got busier during the eight weeks?

F

Here are the total prices per week for six package holidays to Spain.

£285.50	£345.80	£398	£648.50	£423.40	£472.30

1 Find the range of the prices for the holidays.
2 Do you think that all of them will be in the same kind of accommodation?
3 When Simon goes to book his holiday, the most expensive holiday is unavailable. What is the range of the remaining holidays?

Now look back at your work in this lesson.
- How do you find the range of any set of data?
- What happens to the range of a set of values if you take away the highest or lowest number? What happens to the range if you take away one of the numbers in the middle of the set of values?

③ Probability order

Lunar eclipses can be seen from any spot on the Earth (as long as the Moon is visible). Solar eclipses can only be seen from certain places on the Earth at any one time. Which kind of eclipse do you think you are most likely to see within the next year?

1 Which of the following events are impossible?
The Sun will not shine for a month.
There will be 31 days in February next year.
There will be a thunderstorm in the next week.
2 Which of these events is very unlikely to happen?
You will grow 15 cm by your next birthday.
You will be the first to finish this exercise in the class.
You will be let off your homework tonight.
3 Write down three things that are possible but unlikely.

Two long straws and a shorter one are placed so that all the top ends are level and the bottom ends are hidden.

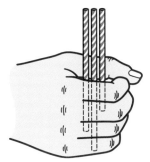

1 What is the chance of picking the short straw? Write your answer as a fraction.
2 What is the chance of picking a long straw? Write your answer as a fraction.
3 Add together these fractions. What do you notice about your answer?
4 If there were four long straws and one short straw, what is the chance of picking the short straw?

C

1. Count up how many pupils there are in your class. How many are girls? How many are boys?

2. If you put all the names of the pupils in your class in a hat and pick one out without looking, is it more likely that a boy is chosen? Give a reason for your answer.

3. If you roll a dice in a game, is there a greater chance of an odd number or even number being scored? Give a reason for your answer.

D

Here are some things that could happen when you get home tonight.

> You will have a meal.
> It will rain.
> It will get dark.
> You will finish all your homework.
> You will go out with your friends.
> You will go to bed before midnight.

1. Write down one of these things that is certain to happen.
2. Choose another that is very likely to happen.
3. Now think of something of your own that is likely to occur.

E

Here is a probability line for events that range from impossible to certain.

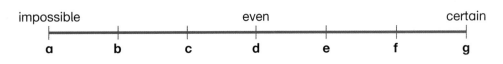

For each of the following statements, choose a letter on the line that shows how likely the statement is. (Your answers may be different from others in your class.)

1. Next year New Year's Day will be in January.
2. You will eat a meal tonight.
3. The next baby born in your family will be a girl.
4. In ten years' time most families will own a helicopter.
5. You will not have a cold for a whole year.
6. You will have children one day.
7. Pigs will grow wings and fly.

Now look back at your work in this lesson.
- Why is putting things in probability order better than using the phrases *more likely* and *less likely*?
- Draw a probability scale and write in values between impossible and certain.

④ Fairness

Someone will have to tell the head!
How can you choose fairly who will go?

Steven and Bev are going to play a board game with a six-sided dice. They need to decide who will go first.

1 Write down which two of the following methods would be a fair way of deciding.

a The first to throw a six starts the game.

b Bev starts if the dice shows numbers 1 or 2, and Steven starts if the dice shows the other numbers.

c Each throws the dice once and the highest scorer begins.

2 Why did you reject the other one?

There is a popular school outing leaving next week. All the pupils want to go, but there are only ten places available.

1 Which of the following ways of choosing the ten pupils would be fairest?

a The teacher chooses the pupils.

b The first ten pupils that bring in the money go on the trip.

c Ten names are drawn from a hat containing all the names.

d Leave the pupils to choose the ten themselves.

2 Give a reason for your answer.

3 Explain why one of the other methods could be unfair.

C

There are two green balls and one blue ball in a bag. Jacob and Marian both pick a ball without looking.

1 If Jacob picks first, which colour is he most likely to get?
2 Can you say why this is so?
3 Jacob actually picks a green ball. Marian picks from the remaining two. What chance has she got of getting the blue one?
4 Why is Marian's chance different from Jacob's?

D

After their cricket ball has broken the glass in the school greenhouse, Ray and his team need someone to tell the Head. Ray suggests that they take 11 straws, cut one short and hold the ends even. The team member that picks the short straw will get the task!

1 Is the first person to draw a straw likely to get the short one?
2 What is the chance that the second person will get the short one?
3 If the first nine straws drawn are all long, what chance has the tenth person of getting the last long straw?
4 Would you choose to go first or last?
5 How could the captain fairly choose the order of who picks?

E

1 Think of two fair ways that could be used to decide which team kicks off a football match.
2 Think of a fair way to decide which of the four players serves first in a doubles game of tennis.

Now look back at your work in this lesson.
- Think of a fair way of choosing who will get a free ticket to an important event.
- What alternatives are there to making a 'blind choice'?

⑤ Probability scale

Identical twins look exactly the same, so you have an *even chance* of getting their names the wrong way round. What is your chance of being right? What numbers can we use for even chance?

Before starting these exercises, draw a probability line. Label it from 0 at one end to 1 at the other, and put ½, 0.5 or 50% in the centre (whichever you find easiest). Label other points as you need them.

```
├──────────────────────────┼──────────────────────────┤
0                         0.5                          1
```

Jake has identical twin baby brothers, Josh and Zak.

1 One of the babies is crying. What is the probability that, when Jake goes to find out what is wrong, it will be Zak crying?

2 Aunt Judy can never tell the babies apart. She calls the first one she picks up Josh each time. What chance has she of being right?

3 If one of the babies throws his bread and butter on the floor, what is the chance it will land butter side down?

4 Mark the position for your answers with an **A** on your probability line.

1 Janice picks a card from a full pack. What is the chance her card will be a club?

2 Write down another event that will have the same probability.

3 Mark the chance you found for Janice's card on the probability line with a **B**.

At the end of a card game there are four cards left in a pile.

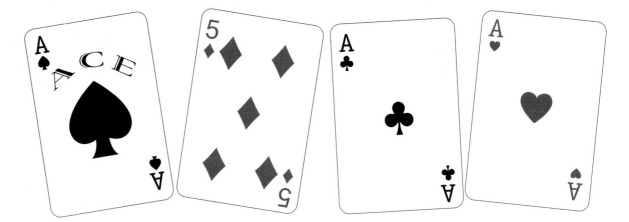

1 Erin needs an ace to win. What is her chance of picking a winning card?

2 Write down another event that will have the same probability.

3 Mark this point on the line with a letter **C**.

1 Class 9A asked 100 pupils at their school which colour they would prefer for the new school sweatshirt: *red* or *blue*. 60 pupils chose red. Mark the probability that any one of these pupils would choose blue on the probability line with the letter **D**.

E

Mr Shah bought 50 tulip bulbs last year. In the spring, 45 of them flowered.

1 What is the probability that one of these bulbs chosen at random didn't flower? Mark this probability on your line with the letter **E**.

2 This year, he is buying his tulip bulbs from a different shop. The shop claims that 80% of bulbs will produce flowers. Is that a better or worse chance than last year's bulbs?

F

1 Estimate the probability that next Christmas Day there will be more than 10 cm of snow in London. Think about recent winters to help with your estimate. Mark a point **F** on your line to show what you think the chance is.

2 What event could be represented by a 99% probability?

Now look back at your work in this lesson.
- How accurately can you show events on a probability scale?
- What advantages does a probability scale have over putting things in order of how likely they are?

⑥ Probability and data

When you pick one thing up at random from a collection of things, you are certain to pick something from within the range. The chance of picking something depends on how frequently it exists within the sample. The most likely item will be the mode.

On the first day back at school after the summer break, the pupils in class 7b were asked to do a survey to find out what kind of transport they had used on the way to their holiday destination. The choices were: ferry, aeroplane, train, car, bike, helicopter, coach or walking. Here are the results of the survey.

1. Using a tally, find out how many pupils used each type of transport.
2. Display your findings in a table.
3. Which kind of travel was the one used most frequently?
4. What is this most popular item known as?

Jackie timed her journey to school each morning for two weeks. The times she wrote down are given below.

36 minutes	27 minutes	32 minutes	24 minutes	28 minutes
28 minutes	31 minutes	29 minutes	25 minutes	30 minutes

1. What was the shortest time that she took?
2. How long did her slowest journey take?
3. Write down the range of the times taken.
4. Jackie needs to get to school by 9:00 a.m. What time would you advise her to leave home each morning?
5. If she leaves home at 8:25 a.m., what is the chance that she arrives in time for school?

C Place these five events on a probability line according to whether you think they are impossible, certain, likely, unlikely or if they have an even chance of happening.

1 If you buy two packets of biscuits with six in each, you will have 12 biscuits in total.

2 If you book your summer holiday in Wales in June, you are sure to get a sunny week.

3 Every five years, your birthday will fall on a different date.

4 You will need some new clothes before the end of the year.

5 When you choose one ball from a bag that contains six red, three blue, two green and one white one, you will get a red one.

D Mark the following events along a probability line according to how likely they are. Label them using the letters **a** to **f**. You may use % or fractions along your line if you prefer.

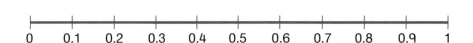

a Someone in the world will sneeze tomorrow.

b The next baby born at the local hospital will be a boy.

c The next person you meet will have their birthday in the spring.

d There are ten balls, all of different colours, in a bag. If Alice picks one at random, what is the probability that she will choose a red one?

e There are 28 pupils in Gail's class, 21 boys and seven girls. What is the probability that a boy will win a prize draw if they all have one ticket?

f If a dice is tossed, a number *less than* 3 will be obtained.

E Explain why two of the following are fair methods of choosing and the other is unfair.

1 A coin is tossed and the team which chooses heads or tails correctly gets to go first.

2 The tallest pupils in the class are chosen to be in the football team.

3 The winner of a lottery is the person whose ticket is chosen at random from a box containing all the tickets.

> Now look back at your work in this lesson.
> * What can the range or the mode tell you about a set of data? Do you need anything else to understand the data?
> * How do you work out the probability of something happening from a set of data?

Module **F**7

Number and algebra

❶ *If* this *then* that!

Understanding conditional instructions, using words such as *if* and *then*, in mathematical situations

❷ This *and* that, but *not* the other!

Using instructions that contain the logical meaning of the words *and* and *not,* in mathematical situations

❸ Following instructions

Using sets of rules that involve number sequences and relationships between number columns

❹ Spreadsheets

Understanding how a spreadsheet is used. Finding a formula for a cell which uses another cell

❺ Working with formulas

Replacing symbols in formulas (or rules) with different values and finding the results

❻ Solving equations

Solving equations by trial and improvement. Finding the value that produces the given result

Key words and phrases

condition
criteria
even
instruction
multiple
odd
selection
sequence

algebraically
cell
column
equation
formula
number sentence
row
solve
spreadsheet
substitute
value
variable

① *If* this *then* that!

The people are trying to find a perfect partner by answering questions about their age, their interests and their personality. The type of person that the dating agency chooses for them depends on the answers that they give. Questions or instructions where the outcome depends on something are called *conditional*.

1 Work together as a class. Listen to these instructions from your teacher.
- If your birthday comes between March and December (inclusive), *stand up.*
- For those standing up – if your birthday is between September and the end of the year (inclusive), *sit down.*
- For those standing up – if you are male, *sit down.*
- For those standing up – if you have short hair, *sit down.*
- For those standing up – if you hate football, *sit down.*

2 The people standing up should be long-haired females, born between March and August, who don't mind football. Is that the case?

3 How many pupils will be standing up in an all-boys class?

1 Follow these instructions carefully.
- If you are male then draw a straight line across the page.
- If you are female then draw a straight line up the page.
- If you were born in March, April or May then draw a wavy line next to your straight line.
- If you have any pets, then put one dot next to the line for each pet that you have.

2 Now look at the instructions again and write down what you can tell about the pupils who drew the following things.

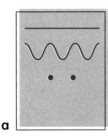
a

b

c

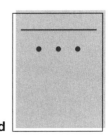
d

Now look at these number lists.

| 30 | 820 | 45 | 6 | 2 | 78 | 809 | 1006 | 105 | 452 | 78 | 32 | 56 |

1 Copy this list of numbers. If a number is even, then *underline it*. If a number is odd, then *draw a circle round it*.

| 9.6 | 9.8 | 9.1 | 9.01 | 9.03 | 9.04 | 9.9 | 9.657 |

2 Copy this list of numbers. If a number is bigger than 9.5, underline it.

| 23 | 55 | 50 | 62 | 45 | 25 | 20 | 70 | 80 | 41 |

3 Copy out numbers from the list above that are multiples of 5.

4 Write down the names of days in the week that contain the letter 't'.

Starting on square 1, follow the instructions on this maze. Where do you end up?

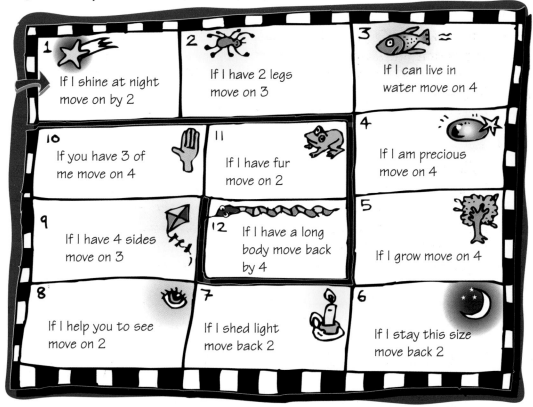

Now look back at your work in this lesson
- How do you follow instructions that include if... then... ?
- How do you check that you have followed the instructions correctly?

② This *and* that, but *not* the other!

The champion dog has shiny hair of only one colour *and* weighs less than 15 kg, but does *not* have any accessories like glasses or bows. Can you spot which dog was the champion?

 Imagine you have the chance to design a common room for your year group to use at lunch time.

1 Write down two things that the room should have.

2 Write down one thing that the room should not have.

3 Now compare your list with one of your friends' list. See if you can agree on two things the common room should have and one thing it should not have. Write down your new list.

 The Patel family wants to buy a house that has three bedrooms and a garage, but does not have a large garden. Which of the following houses, labelled **a** to **d**, should they go to look at?

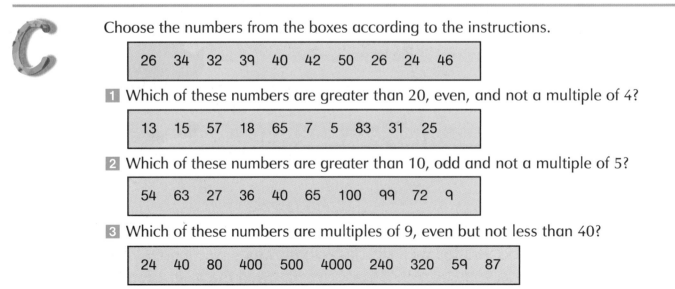

HANSTONES Estate Agents

22 Apple Lane

3 bedrooms, semi-detached house with large gardens, a conservatory and permission to build a garage.

a

HANSTONES Estate Agents

34 Brown Court

3 bedroom home on a new estate, with a garage, front patio and a small back garden.

b

HANSTONES Estate Agents

16 Canada Ridge

Terraced house with 3 bedrooms, an attic, street parking space and a small front garden.

c

HANSTONES Estate Agents

44 Dream Street

2 bedroom town house, with small garden and garage.

d

Choose the numbers from the boxes according to the instructions.

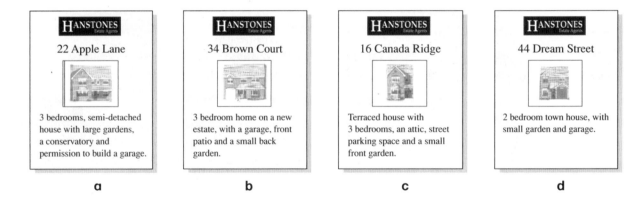

| 26 | 34 | 32 | 39 | 40 | 42 | 50 | 26 | 24 | 46 |

1 Which of these numbers are greater than 20, even, and not a multiple of 4?

| 13 | 15 | 57 | 18 | 65 | 7 | 5 | 83 | 31 | 25 |

2 Which of these numbers are greater than 10, odd and not a multiple of 5?

| 54 | 63 | 27 | 36 | 40 | 65 | 100 | 99 | 72 | 9 |

3 Which of these numbers are multiples of 9, even but not less than 40?

| 24 | 40 | 80 | 400 | 500 | 4000 | 240 | 320 | 59 | 87 |

4 Which of these numbers are multiple of 10, multiples of 4 and an odd number?

D

After their GCSE exams, a group of Year 11 friends are planning a holiday together. They each make a list of the price they can afford. They also write down one thing they like and one they don't like. It turns out that the holiday must be:

- less than £300
- on the coast
- not a quiet place

1 Look at this travel agent's window and decide which holidays they should consider.

2 Explain why the other holidays were unsuitable.

E

Mina is looking for a part-time job. The job must be indoors, start no earlier than 4:00 p.m. and be no more than three evenings per week. Which of the following jobs could she choose?

Now look back at your work in this lesson.

- How do you select from a list using two or three instructions?
- Do you have a special way of remembering instructions that say you *must have* some things but *must not have* other things?

③ Following instructions

Sometimes you give instructions, other times you must follow instructions.
What instructions have you given this week?
What instructions have you followed?

1 Copy this sequence and add the next three numbers.

2   4   8   ✿ ✿ ✿

2 What instructions would you give to a friend if you wanted them to continue the sequence in question 1?

3 Can you spot the rule in the list of numbers below?

90	10	80	70	20	60	50

4 Write down some rules that describe the numbers below.

12	15	18	21	24	27

Continue each of these lists until there are 10 numbers. In each case follow the rule below.

> The next number is made by adding the previous two numbers.

1 2, 2, 4, 6, 10, ⊚, ⊚, ⊚, ⊚, ⊚
2 0, 1, 1, 2, ⊚, ⊚, ⊚, ⊚, ⊚, ⊚
3 0.1, 0.2, 0.3, 0.5, ⊚, ⊚, ⊚, ⊚, ⊚, ⊚
4 10, 40, 50, ⊚, ⊚, ⊚, ⊚, ⊚, ⊚, ⊚
5 7, 8, 15, ⊚, ⊚, ⊚, ⊚, ⊚, ⊚, ⊚

Write down the rule for each of these sequences of numbers.
1 48   24   12   6   3   1.5   0.75 ...
2 100   200   400   800   1600 ...
3 2   20   200   2000   20 000 ...
4 2½   3   3½   4   4½ ...
5 ½   ⅓   ¼   ⅕   ⅙ ...

D

1 Choose any number between 1 and 10 to start a sequence. The next number in the sequence is double the one before it. Write down the first six numbers in the sequence.

2 Choose any multiple of 10 to start a sequence. The next number in the sequence is half the one before it. Write down the first four numbers in the sequence.

3 Choose any two numbers between 1 and 10 to start a sequence. Adding the previous two numbers makes the next number. Write down the first six numbers in your sequence.

4 Choose any number between 1 and 10 to start your sequence. The next number is ten times the one before it. Write down the first five numbers in the sequence.

E

1 Copy and complete the table so that the third column is the sum of the numbers in the first two columns.

A	B	C
1	10	@
2	20	@
3	30	@
4	40	@
5	50	@
6	60	@

2 Write down the link between the numbers in column B and the numbers in column A.

F

What is the rule that connects the numbers in columns A, B and C below?

A	B	C
10	2	20
4	3	12
6	4	24
10	5	50

Now look back at your work in this lesson.
- Can you follow a set of instructions involving numbers which change?
- How do you find the rule for a set of changing numbers?

④ Spreadsheets

E3	▼	■				
	A	B	C	D	E	F	G
1	Item	Price (£)	No. Items	Net price (£)	Tax (£)	Total	
2	Video cassette	2.95	2	5.9	1.23	7.13	
3	Ink cartridge	4	5				
4							
5							
6							
7							

◄ ◄► ► Sheet 1 / Sheet 2 / Sheet 3 ◄

Ready

In some shops, the checkout screen uses a spreadsheet. A spreadsheet is a table or a grid of columns and rows which are coded. If you type information into some of the cells, other cells are filled automatically with useful information. The computer uses formulas and rules to fill in these cells.

1 How are the columns coded?
2 How are the rows coded?
3 Why do you think the rows and columns use different codes?
4 What does the number in cell C3 mean?
5 How can you work out what goes in cell D3?
6 What formula would all the cells in column D have?
7 What formula do all the cells in column F have?

	A	B	C	D
1	Bus stop	People getting on	People getting off	People on board
2	1	20	0	= B2 − C2
3	2	5	2	= D2 + B2 − C2

1 What is written in cell D2?
2 What does this formula calculate?
3 Why is the formula in D3 different?
4 What does it calculate?

C The blue cell in this spreadsheet has an address of A1. Write down the address of each of the coloured cells in the spreadsheet.

	A	B	C	D
1				
2				
3				

	A	B	C
1	Cost of item	Number bought	Total cost
2	£4	10	= A2 × B2
3	£10	2	= A3 × B3
4	£2	3	= A4 × B4
5	£5	4	= A5 × B5
6			

In each row, the formula in column C calculates the total cost of a purchase. Write down the total cost that would be calculated in the following cells.

1 C2

2 C3

3 C4

4 C5

5 To calculate the total cost of all the shopping in rows 2 to 5, what formula should you type into cell C6?

In a sale, all clothes are now half price.

1 Copy and complete the spreadsheet, putting the correct formula in column C to calculate the new prices.

	A	B	C
1	Item	Full price	Half price
2	jeans	£46	
3	sweatshirt	£26	
4	skirt	£20	
5			

2 Write down the formula that should go in cell C5 to calculate the total cost of the items.

F

1 Design a spreadsheet that works out how much each of these workers earns each week. The manager wants the spreadsheet to work out the wages when she types in the number of hours worked in that week.

Jackie is paid £4.50 per hour and this week she has worked 28 hours.
Ray is on the same pay but has worked 15 hours.
Ashley is paid £6 per hour and has worked 32 hours.

Now look back at your work in this lesson.
- How do you write a formula for a cell in a spreadsheet?
- How do check or change a formula in a spreadsheet?

⑤ Working with formulas

The amount of time that you cook something in a microwave oven depends on what you put in the oven, and also how much of it you put in. The manual for this oven says to cook a medium-sized potato for five minutes. Do you think that the potato in the picture is medium-sized? What should be done to the cooking time for this potato?

1 The cooking time for medium-sized jacket potatoes is found from these instructions.
   • For one potato set for four minutes.
   • For every extra potato, add two minutes.
   How long will it take to cook four potatoes?

2 Explain how this formula works.

> time = 2 × number of potatoes + 2

The roasting time for a chicken is given by the following formula.

> roasting time = 20 × number of pounds + 20 minutes

Write down the number of minutes that you would need to roast each of the following chickens.

1 A chicken weighing 3 pounds
2 A chicken weighing 4 pounds
3 A chicken weighing 4.5 pounds
4 A chicken weighing 2.5 pounds
5 If each of these chickens started cooking at 1 p.m., at what time would they be cooked?

Charges at a bowling alley are calculated using the following formula.

> cost = £3 for first game + £2 × each extra game

How many games were played by each of the following people?

1 Sharon, who paid £5   **3** Ali, who paid £11
2 David, who paid £9   **4** Sue, who paid £7

D

To convert temperatures from degrees Celsius to degrees Fahrenheit the following formula is used:

$$F = 1.8 \times C + 32$$

What is the temperature in degrees Celsius for these temperatures written in degrees Fahrenheit?

1. 10°F
2. 4°F
3. 27°F
4. 18.5°F
5. 0°F

E

A car hire firm charges a fixed rate of £25 plus £20 for each day that a car is hired.

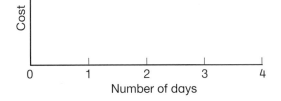

CAR HIRE
£25.00 fixed charge plus £20.00 per day

1. Copy and complete this table of charges.

Number of days	Charge
1	
2	
3	
4	

2. Write down a formula for the charges.

F

1. Draw a graph of the charges in exercise E. Put the number of days on the horizontal axis and the cost on the vertical axis.

Cost

0   1   2   3   4
Number of days

2. Plot points on your graph.
3. Draw a line joining the points.
4. What do you notice about your line?

Now look back at your work in this lesson.
- Can you read and understand a formula?
- Can you put values into a formula and work out the correct answer?

⑥ Solving equations

In this game the numbers in every line, vertical, horizontal and diagonal, have to add up to 15. What two numbers are needed to complete the magic square?

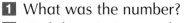

A

> I think of a number, multiply it by 3 and get an answer of 453.

1 What was the number?
2 Find the missing number: ? × 3 = 453
3 Find the value of y if: $y \times 3 = 453$
4 Find the value of y if: $3y = 453$

B

1 Jo thinks of a number, adds 36 and gets the answer 100. What was the number?
2 Ian thinks of a number, subtracts 40 and gets the answer 84. What was the number?
3 Will thinks of a number, doubles it and gets the answer 720. What was the number?
4 Lucy thinks of a number, divides it by 3 and gets the answer 60. What was the number?
5 Ricky think of a number, adds 27 and gets the answer 86. What was the number?

C Find the missing numbers in these equations.
1. ✿ + 12 = 38
2. ✿ − 26 = 80
3. 34 × ✿ = 282
4. 189 ÷ ✿ = 9
5. 256 − ✿ = 188

D
1. Find the value of y if:
$$\boxed{y} + \boxed{45} = \boxed{81}$$
2. Find the value of y if:
$$\boxed{y} - \boxed{18} = \boxed{60}$$
3. Find the value of y if:
$$\boxed{y} \times \boxed{12} = \boxed{132}$$
4. Find the value of y if:
$$\boxed{y} \div \boxed{6} = \boxed{15}$$
5. Find the value of y if:
$$\boxed{y} \div \boxed{120} = \boxed{4}$$
6. Find the value of y if:
$$\boxed{y} \times \boxed{14} = \boxed{168}$$

E
1. Find the value of d if:
$$\boxed{7d} = \boxed{434}$$
2. Find the value of m if:
$$\boxed{m/4} = \boxed{6.5}$$
3. Find the value of c if:
$$\boxed{2.5c} = \boxed{30}$$
4. Find the value of t if:
$$\boxed{10t} = \boxed{146}$$
5. Find the value of r if:
$$\boxed{20r} = \boxed{5}$$
6. Find the value of p if:
$$\boxed{6p} = \boxed{15}$$

F
1. Find the value of y if:
$$\boxed{2y} + \boxed{3} = \boxed{7}$$
2. Find the value of d if:
$$\boxed{3d} + \boxed{1} = \boxed{10}$$
3. Find the value of k if:
$$\boxed{2} + \boxed{3k} = \boxed{5}$$
4. Find the value of g if:
$$\boxed{8g} + \boxed{3} = \boxed{7}$$
5. Find the value of h if:
$$\boxed{10} + \boxed{h/4} = \boxed{20}$$
6. Find the value of f if:
$$\boxed{3} + \boxed{4f} = \boxed{19}$$

Now look back at your work in this lesson.
- How do you find the missing number from a number sentence?
- How do you solve an equation written algebraically?

Module F8

Shape and space

① Type of triangles

Recognising different types of triangles by looking at their sides and angles

② Measuring angles

Using a protractor or an angle maker to measure angles

③ Sliding on the grid

Recognising that a shape has been moved to a new position through a combination of horizontal and vertical movements

④ Symmetry and reflection

Recognising reflection within 2D shapes. Identifying co-ordinates of reflected points

⑤ Rotation and symmetry

Recognising rotational symmetry in 2D and 3D shapes. Identifying which tool can complete a job

⑥ Skills in angles and grids

Practising the skills you have learnt

Key words and phrases

360 degrees
angle around a point, angle on a straight line
angle maker, protractor
arms of an angle
bearing, compass directions
classifying shapes
equilateral triangles, right-angle triangle
isosceles
scalene

co-ordinates
diagonal move, moves on a grid
logo instructions
sliding movement, translation

enlarge by a scale factor of 2
hexagonal cross section
internal angle, external angle of a polygon
line of symmetry, line of reflection
order of rotational symmetry
quadrilateral
reflection
skewed, oblique line of reflection

① Types of triangles

This crocodile has its mouth open at an acute angle. If the angle was any smaller it could get painful for the man! What other types of angle do you know? Draw a picture of a crocodile with its mouth open to show an obtuse angle, a straight angle and a reflex angle.

A Look at these triangles. Study the angles and the lengths of the sides.

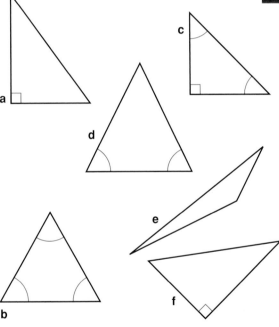

Angles	Triangles
Acute	**Isosceles triangle** has two sides the same and two angles the same
Obtuse	**Scalene triangle** all sides and angles are different
Straight	**Equilateral triangle** all sides are the same length and all angles are equal
Reflex	**Right-angled triangle** a triangle with one square corner and the sides may be of any length

Copy and complete the following sentences.

1 Triangle **a** has __ different sides, and one corner is a _____ angle. It also has __ acute angles.

2 Triangle **b** has __ sides that are the same length, and __ angles that are equal. These angles are acute angles.

3 Triangle **c** has __ sides that are equal, and __ angles that are the same. It also has one _____ angle. It has two _____ angles.

4 Triangle **d** has two sides and two acute angles that are _____.

5 In triangle **e**, all the sides and all the angles are _____. This triangle has two _____ angles and one _____ angle. It is a _____ triangle.

6 Describe triangle **f**.

Look at these shapes.

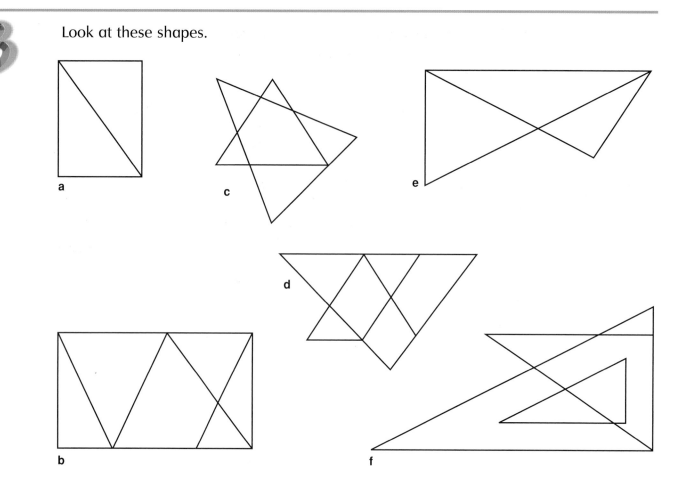

a   b   c   d   e   f

1 Write down how many triangles you can find in each design. Remember a triangle must have three sides. Look for triangles within triangles.

2 Compare your answers with other members of your class and see if any of you have missed some triangles.

Look at the triangles.

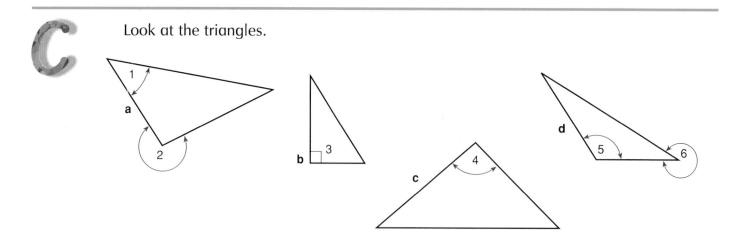

1 Write down the name that we give to each of the angles numbered 1 to 6.

2 Use the information from exercise A to identify the type of triangles labelled **a**, **b**, **c**, and **d**.

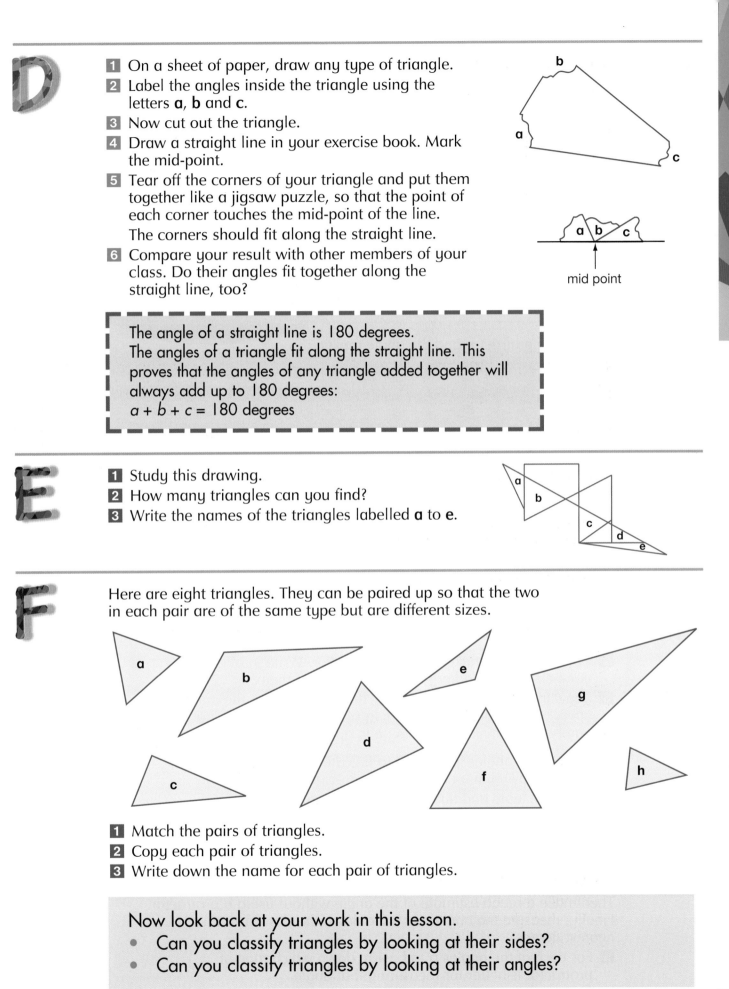

D

1. On a sheet of paper, draw any type of triangle.
2. Label the angles inside the triangle using the letters **a**, **b** and **c**.
3. Now cut out the triangle.
4. Draw a straight line in your exercise book. Mark the mid-point.
5. Tear off the corners of your triangle and put them together like a jigsaw puzzle, so that the point of each corner touches the mid-point of the line.
   The corners should fit along the straight line.
6. Compare your result with other members of your class. Do their angles fit together along the straight line, too?

mid point

> The angle of a straight line is 180 degrees.
> The angles of a triangle fit along the straight line. This proves that the angles of any triangle added together will always add up to 180 degrees:
> a + b + c = 180 degrees

E

1. Study this drawing.
2. How many triangles can you find?
3. Write the names of the triangles labelled **a** to **e**.

F

Here are eight triangles. They can be paired up so that the two in each pair are of the same type but are different sizes.

1. Match the pairs of triangles.
2. Copy each pair of triangles.
3. Write down the name for each pair of triangles.

Now look back at your work in this lesson.
- Can you classify triangles by looking at their sides?
- Can you classify triangles by looking at their angles?

② Measuring angles

Since ancient times, people have measured angles to help them navigate at sea or to study the stars. People decided to break down a full turn into 360 degrees so they could record angles.
Why do you think they chose the number 360?

Look at the protractor and the angle maker.

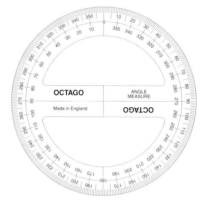

1 Copy and complete these two sentences.
The numbers on the protractor go from 0 degrees to _____.
The numbers on the angle maker (circular protractor) go from 0 degrees to _____.

2 Copy the angle maker and the protractor. Write in a few numbers but you do not need to copy all of them.

3 Draw in a curved arrow to show the direction that the angles open. (Most protractors have two sets of numbers. The outside numbers and inside numbers go in opposite directions.)

4 Look at the angles labelled **a** to **f**. Write whether the arrow for each is moving in a clockwise or anti-clockwise direction.

5 Copy the table and fill in the gaps for angles **a** to **f**.

Angle	More or less than 90 degrees	Estimate of angle (nearest 10 degrees)	Accurate measurement
a			

First decide whether the angle is bigger or smaller than a right angle. Then make a rough estimate of the angle without using a protractor. Finally, measure the angle and write down the answer to the nearest degree.

6 For each of the angles **a** to **f**, write down which type of protractor is better for measuring that angle.

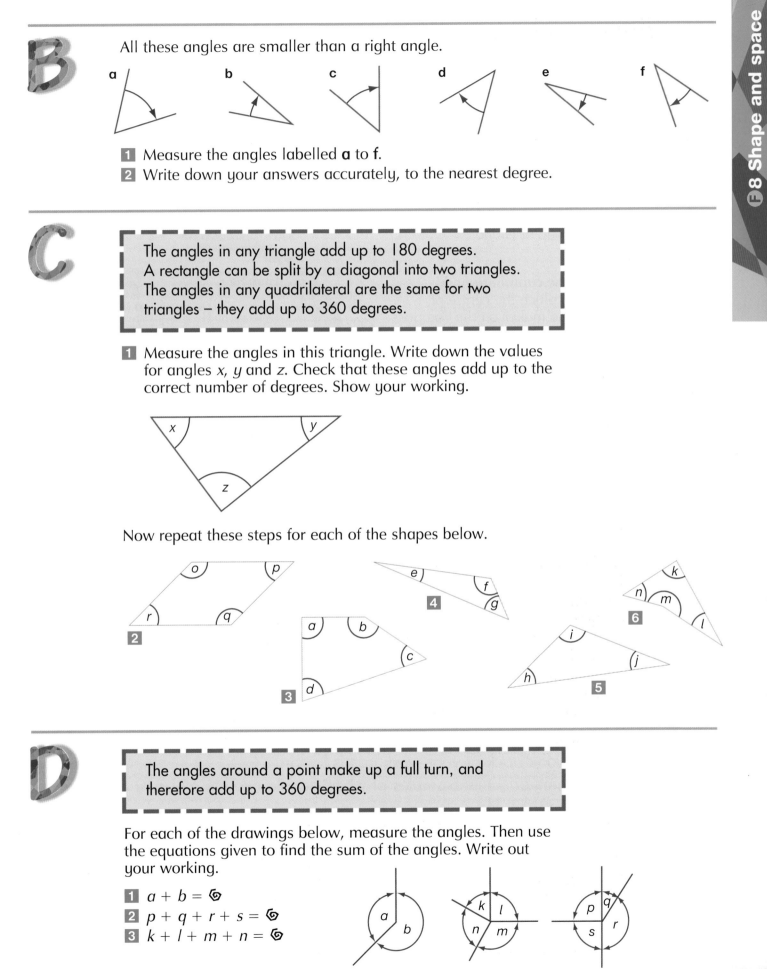

B

All these angles are smaller than a right angle.

a   b   c   d   e   f

1 Measure the angles labelled **a** to **f**.
2 Write down your answers accurately, to the nearest degree.

C

> The angles in any triangle add up to 180 degrees.
> A rectangle can be split by a diagonal into two triangles.
> The angles in any quadrilateral are the same for two
> triangles – they add up to 360 degrees.

1 Measure the angles in this triangle. Write down the values
for angles x, y and z. Check that these angles add up to the
correct number of degrees. Show your working.

Now repeat these steps for each of the shapes below.

2   **3**   **4**   **5**   **6**

D

> The angles around a point make up a full turn, and
> therefore add up to 360 degrees.

For each of the drawings below, measure the angles. Then use
the equations given to find the sum of the angles. Write out
your working.

1 $a + b = $ 🌀
2 $p + q + r + s = $ 🌀
3 $k + l + m + n = $ 🌀

E

For each question, draw a base line of 6 cm and then draw in another arm to show the following angles.

1 75 degrees   **4** 278 degrees

2 17 degrees   **5** 169 degrees

3 125 degrees   **6** 333 degrees

7 Did you have to measure the length of the other arm in each angle?

F

A ship, H.M.S. Nero, is lost in this group of islands.

To help the captain to find his bearings, place the centre of your angle maker on the compass centre. Point 0 towards north. To find the bearing of something, read the angle in a clockwise direction. You can then write down the bearing using three digits.

Bearings always contain three digits. For example, 90 degrees is written as 090 degrees.

For each of the landmarks, write down their bearings.

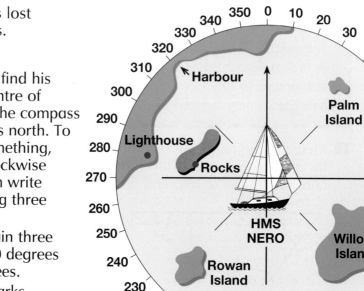

1 Harbour

2 Lighthouse

3 Palm Island

4 Rowan Island

5 Willow Island (give the bearings of both ends of the island)

6 Rocks (give the bearings of both ends of the rocks)

7 The captain wants to reach the harbour on the mainland, avoiding the rocks. Give the compass directions and bearings that he has to take.

Now look back at your work in this lesson.
- Think of some examples of when people need to measure angles in everyday life.
- How do you know that the angles of a triangle add up to 180 degrees?

③ Sliding on the grid

In the game of chess, a knight moves in two steps. First it moves two squares in one direction. This can be forwards, backwards, left or right. Then it moves one square at a right angle to the first step.

One of this knight's possible moves is drawn for you. Can you identify any of the other squares this knight can move to? Why do you think this movement on a grid is called *translation*?

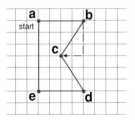

Study the shapes and write down the answers to the questions.

1 Starting at **a**, give instructions on how to get from **a** to **b**, then from **b** to **c**, from **c** to **d** and finally back to **a** again.

2 Give instructions on how to move from **a** to **b**, from **b** to **c** and from **c** to **a**, using only moves to the left, right, up or down.

3 Repeat question 2, but this time use bearings.

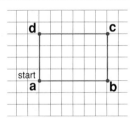

4 Use compass readings (north, east, south or west) to describe how to move from **a** to **b**, from **b** to **c**, from **c** to **d**, from **d** to **e** and from **e** to **a**.

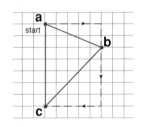

5 Copy the grid and shapes.
Give the co-ordinates of corners **a**, **b**, **c** and **d** for the shaded shape.
Now label the corners in the new position of the s hape and write down the co-ordinates.
Finally, write down how many squares and in what direction the shape has moved.

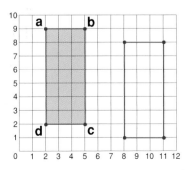

B

For each of these questions, you will need a grid of 10 squares × 10 squares on squared paper. Read the logo instructions and then answer the questions by plotting points on your grids and joining up the points as you go.

> F = move forwards by the number of squares written after the letter
> B = move backwards by the number of squares written after the letter
> R = turn right by the number of degrees written after the letter
> L = turn left by the number of degrees written after the letter

1. Starting at the bottom left corner of your grid and moving up the page, plot these moves.
   F 5   R 90   F 5   R 90   F 5   R 90   F 5

2. Starting at the bottom right corner of your grid and moving up the page, plot these moves.
   F 8   L 90   F 4   L 90   F 8   L 90   F 4

3. Starting at the bottom left corner of your grid and moving up the page, plot these moves.
   F 5   R 90   F 5   R 135   F 7.2
   Write down the name of the type of shape you have made.

4. Draw any rectangle in your grid and then write down the logo instructions you have used to draw the shape.

5. Draw any triangle in your grid and then write down the logo instructions you have used to draw the shape. You will need a protractor and a ruler to make your instructions accurate.

C

Use these compass directions to help you do the tasks below.

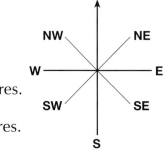

1. a   Draw a cross in the middle of some squared paper. Write the letter **a** next to it.
   b   Move south by three squares and west by three squares. Draw a cross and label it **b**.
   c   Move south by three squares and then east by three squares. Draw a cross and label it **c**.
   d   Move east by three squares and then north by three squares. Draw a cross and label it **d**.

   Now join up the crosses and write down what shape you have made.

2. a   Draw a cross in the middle of another piece of squared paper. Write the letter **a** next to it.
   b   Move north by four squares and then east by one square. Draw a cross and label it **b**.
   c   Move east by six squares. Draw a cross and label it **c**.
   d   Move south by four squares, and then west by one square. Draw a cross and label it **d**.

   Now join up the crosses and describe the type of shape you have made.

Read carefully the information about types of shapes.

Rectangle
two long sides of equal length
two shorter sides of equal length
all the corners are right angles

Rhombus
four equal sides
opposite sides are parallel
opposite angles are the same

Square (a special type of rectangle)
four sides are the same length
all the corners are right angles

Trapezium
four sides
one pair of sides are parallel

Kite
two pairs of equal sides that are not
opposite each other

1 Draw one of these shapes on some squared paper.

2 Write instructions, using compass directions and numbers of squares, so that someone else in your class can draw the shape.

3 Swap your instructions with another member of your class and try to draw the shape they have described. Did the instructions work?

In a translation each point moves the same distance without turning. Copy these grids and the shapes on them. For each one follow the instructions and draw the position of the new shapes, and write the co-ordinates of the new points.

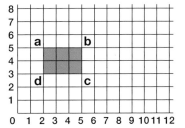

1 Move each point to the left by four squares.

2 Move each point to the right by five squares.

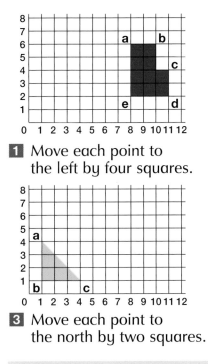

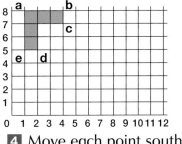

3 Move each point to the north by two squares.

4 Move each point south by three squares and then east by one square.

Now look back at your work in this lesson.
* What effect does a translation have on a shape?
* How many ways can you describe a translation of a shape?

④ Symmetry and reflection

The pop group Abba used reflective symmetry to create a memorable logo.
We can describe mirror reflections in different ways. When the shapes are regular we can use co-ordinates for accurate descriptions. If you change the angle of a mirror, does the image stay the same?

1 Carefully copy this shape and the mirror on to squared paper.

2 Count the number of squares from each of the dots to the mirror. Write down your results like this: **a** is 3 units from the mirror.

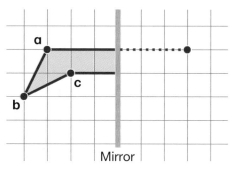

3 For each point, count this number of squares on the other side of the mirror line, and then mark a new point on your grid.

4 Join up the dots to form the new shape.

5 Using the same method, copy the right angled triangle and plot the new shape after it has been reflected.

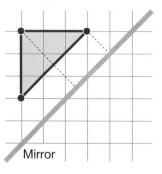

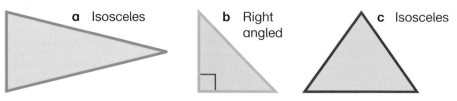

a Isosceles **b** Right angled **c** Isosceles

6 Trace these triangles on to a piece of paper and then carefully cut them out.
Fold each triangle in half to find its line of symmetry. Use a ruler to draw a line along the fold.
This is the mirror line, or the line of reflection.

B Copy each of these shapes on to squared paper and then draw their reflection.

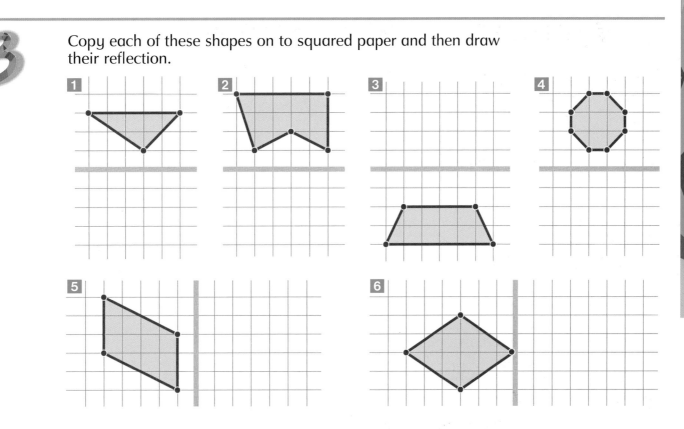

7 Name the shapes in questions 3, 4, 5 and 6.

C Find out which of the quadrilaterals labelled **a** to **f** have lines of symmetry by following these instructions.

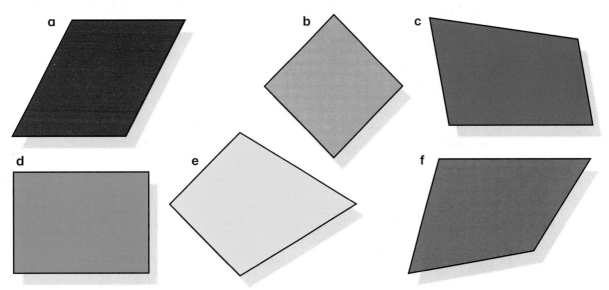

1 Trace the shapes.
2 Carefully cut out the shapes.
3 Try to fold each shape in half, so that one half fits perfectly over the other. Will the shape fold in half more than once?
4 Draw lines on each shape to show the lines of symmetry.
5 Stick the shapes in your book and write next to them any names of quadrilaterals that you recognise.

D

1 Copy or trace these shapes.

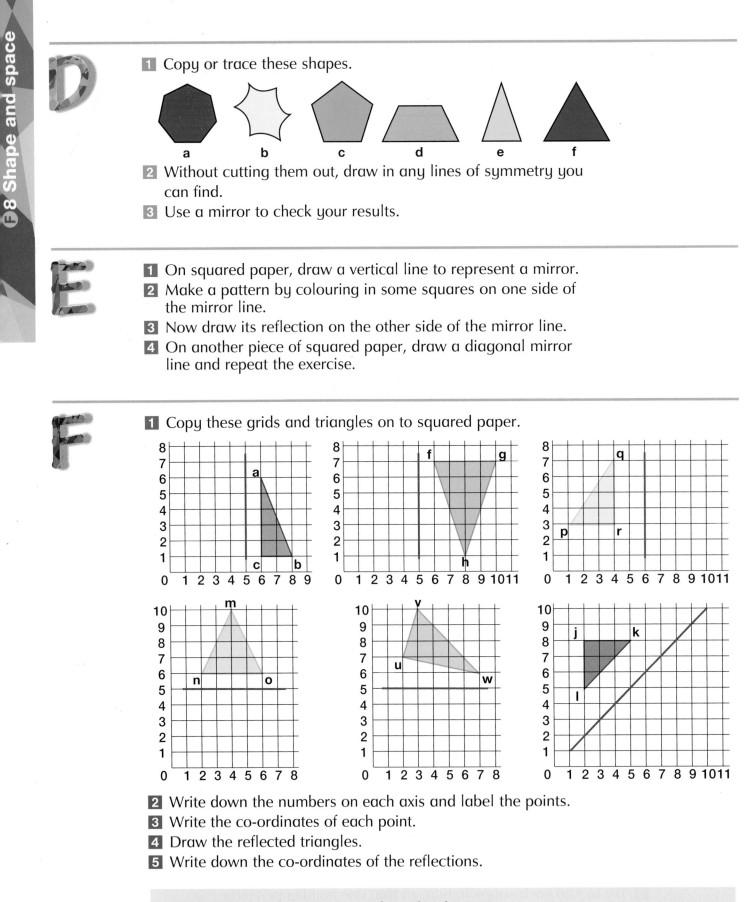

a   b   c   d   e   f

2 Without cutting them out, draw in any lines of symmetry you can find.

3 Use a mirror to check your results.

E

1 On squared paper, draw a vertical line to represent a mirror.

2 Make a pattern by colouring in some squares on one side of the mirror line.

3 Now draw its reflection on the other side of the mirror line.

4 On another piece of squared paper, draw a diagonal mirror line and repeat the exercise.

F

1 Copy these grids and triangles on to squared paper.

2 Write down the numbers on each axis and label the points.

3 Write the co-ordinates of each point.

4 Draw the reflected triangles.

5 Write down the co-ordinates of the reflections.

Now look back at your work in this lesson.
- How do you reflect a shape on a grid for any mirror line?
- Write down the steps you use when you reflect a shape in a mirror line.

⑤ Rotation and symmetry

These sky divers have to concentrate very hard to keep their formation thousands of feet up in the air. What order of rotational symmetry is the shape that they are making?

1 Which of these flags have rotational symmetry?

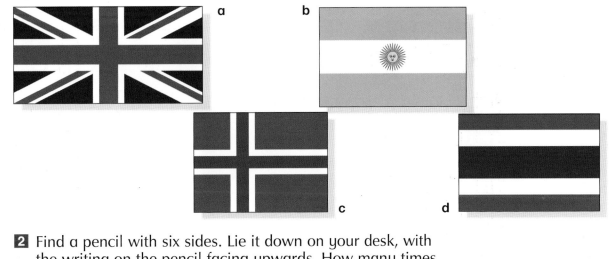

a b c d

2 Find a pencil with six sides. Lie it down on your desk, with the writing on the pencil facing upwards. How many times can you roll the pencil until it returns to the original side?
Copy and complete this sentence:
The hexagonal pencil has rotational symmetry order _____ .

3 Count the spokes on this bicycle wheel to find the order of rotational symmetry.
Copy and complete this sentence:
The bicycle wheel has rotational symmetry order _____ .

B

Write down the order of rotational symmetry for these shapes.

C

Look at these 3D shapes. Match each tool with the object that it fits.

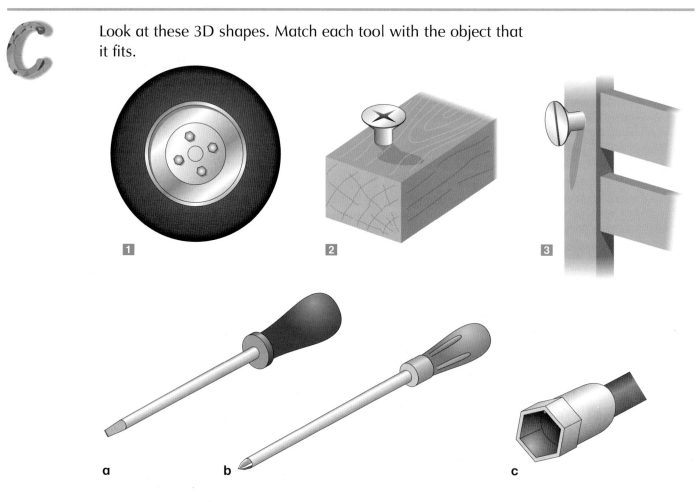

4 Write down the order of rotational symmetry for each object.

D

1 Trace or copy the designs labelled **a** to **c**.

a   b   c

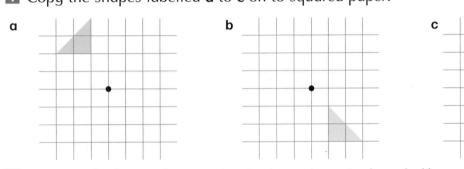 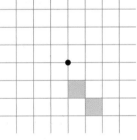

2 Write down the order of rotational symmetry for each shape.
3 Add four squares to each shape, so that the order of rotational symmetry remains the same.

E

1 Copy the shapes labelled **a** to **c** on to squared paper.

a   b   c

2 Draw each shape after rotating it about the point by a half turn.
3 Draw each shape after rotating it about the point by a quarter turn in a clockwise direction.

F

1 Copy the shape and the centre of rotation on to squared paper.

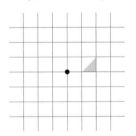

2 Draw the shape after it has been enlarged by scale factor 2. This means that each corner of the new shape is twice the distance from the centre point than in the original shape.
3 Now rotate your new shape by a quarter turn and draw it in the next position.
4 Repeat step 3 until you return to the original shape.

Now look back at your work in this lesson.
- Give some examples of everyday objects with rotational symmetry.
- Can you think of any uses for rotational symmetry?

⑥ Skills in angles and grids

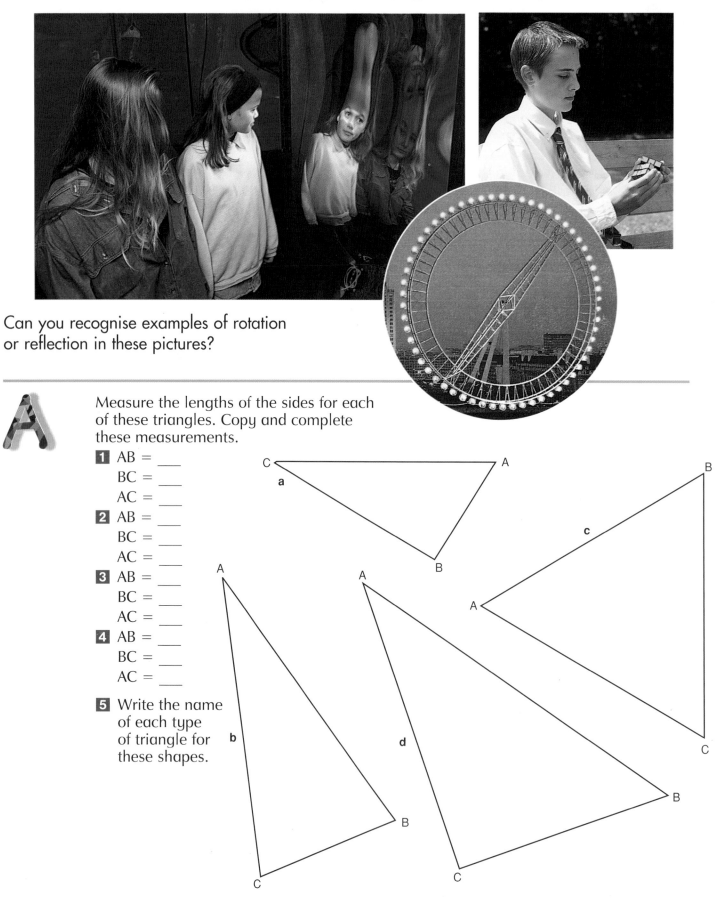

Can you recognise examples of rotation
or reflection in these pictures?

Measure the lengths of the sides for each
of these triangles. Copy and complete
these measurements.

1 AB = ___
BC = ___
AC = ___

2 AB = ___
BC = ___
AC = ___

3 AB = ___
BC = ___
AC = ___

4 AB = ___
BC = ___
AC = ___

5 Write the name
of each type
of triangle for
these shapes.

Measure the angles of each of the triangles in exercise A and then complete these statements.

1 Triangle **a**:
angle at A =
angle B =
angle at C =
total =

2 Triangle **b**:
angle at A =
angle B =
angle at C =
total =

3 Triangle **c**:
angle at A =
angle B =
angle at C =
total =

4 Triangle **d**:
angle at A =
angle B =
angle at C =
total =

5 Check that each total adds up to about 180 degrees.

Look at these shapes and then answer the questions. Use your answers to complete the table.

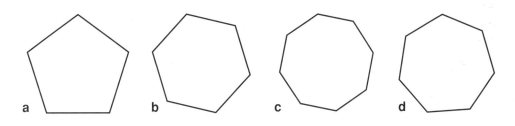

a   b   c   d

1 Write down the number of sides that each shape has.
2 Measure the internal angles of each shape.
3 Measure the external angles of each shape using an angle maker.

Name of shape	Number of sides	Internal angle	External angle
a			
b			
c			
d			

Copy these shapes on to squared paper.

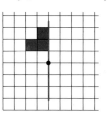
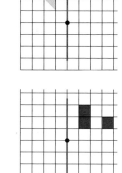

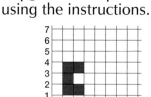

1 Mark in the mirror line and the centre point as shown.
2 Draw in reflections of the shapes.

Using your drawings from exercise D, rotate the shapes around each centre point by 90 degrees clockwise.

Copy these shapes on to squared paper and translate each shape using the instructions.

1 Move right 4 squares.

2 Move north 3 squares.

3 Move west 2 squares.

4 Move south 3 squares.

5 Move right 4 squares, up 2 squares.

6 Move left 3 squares, down 2 squares.

Now look back at your work in this lesson.
- Name all the different types of triangles.
- Write down simple instructions on how to do a reflection, a translation and a rotation of a shape on a grid?

Module F5–F8

Review your skills

Number and algebra

1. Mary went to bed at 11:00 p.m. and slept for seven hours. What time did she wake up?

2. Joe went to bed at 10:30 p.m. and slept for nine hours. What time did he wake up?

3. Samuel measures the width of the play cabin in the garden to be 4 units, and Verity makes it 48 units. Who is using inches and who is using feet?

4. True or false? I can swim under water for an hour or two.

5. Suppose you are in Cambridge and there is a train from Cambridge to London every hour, at 10 minutes past the hour. The journey lasts about an hour. If you have to be in London at half past nine in the morning, what is the latest train you could take?

Handling data

In a mountain cycling race the times taken by 10 cyclists were:

3 hours 50 minutes	2 hours 38 minutes
2 hours 17 minutes	3 hours 1 minute
3 hours 20 minutes	2 hours 49 minutes
2 hours 41 minutes	2 hours 59 minutes
2 hours 28 minutes	3 hours 10 minutes

1. What were the fastest and slowest times?
2. Write down the range of the times.
3. If the race started at 10:30 a.m., what time did the last cyclist complete the race?

Draw a probability line like the one below and mark the numbers of the following events along it, according to their likelihood. You may use percentages or fractions along your line if you prefer.

4. A baby will be born in Britain tomorrow.
5. If a die is tossed a number less than 5 will be obtained.

Number and algebra

Year 10 pupils were asked to draw a picture frame and put in it the following symbols to represent their hopes after year 11.

- a pen if they wanted to continue their studies
- a car if they wanted to move out of the area
- a ring if they wanted to get married
- a pram if they wanted to have children

Match the pictures to the pupils.

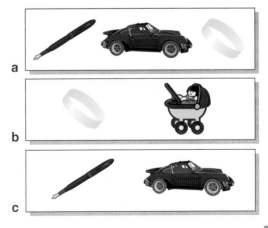

1. Paul wants to continue studies away from his home town. He doesn't intend to get married yet.

2 Mohammed wants to work in the local zoo, get married and have a family.

3 Mary wants to get married and continue studying abroad.

What is the rule for each of these sequences of numbers?

4 2000, 1000, 500, 250

5 12½, 12, 11½, 11, 10½

Charges at a laser zone are calculated using the following formula
Cost = £5 first game + £2 x each extra game

6 Sarah paid £5. How many games did she play?

7 David paid £9. How many games did he play?

Find the missing number.

8 ★ + 14 = 39

9 ★ − 29 = 90

10 41 × ★ = 246

Shape and space

Name the angles without measuring them.

4 Copy the shape on to squared paper and translate it eight units east and two units south.

5 Measure angle 3 to the nearest degree.

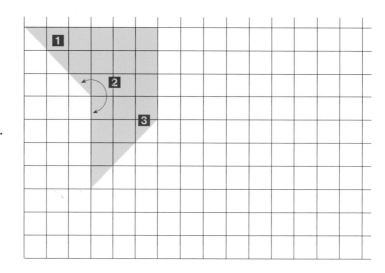

Now try this...

After their exams a group of friends are planning a day trip.
They each write **two things** they would like from the trip. They agree on the following:

- it must not be indoors
- it must cost less than £16 each
- it must be active

Write down the **different** choices that are possible from the following:

- Madame Tussaud's waxworks museum at £15 each
- Bird watching on the Norfolk Broads at £15 each
- Alton Towers theme park at £14 each
- Go-carting at £22 each
- Paintballing at £16 each
- Oasis water activity centre at £13 each

Check your skills

You can check how well you can do the things listed here. Get your parents and friends to help.

Number and algebra

1 I know how to convert different units of measuring time to solve problems.

2 I understand the departure and arrival times shown in a timetable to find out which journeys are possible or not.

3 I know what happens to the numerical value of measurement if a larger or smaller unit is used.

4 I know the likely accuracy of measurements given in a familiar situation.

5 I know the range of temperatures that are likely on normal winter and summer days.

Handling data

1 I can find the mode in a set of data.

2 I can calculate and use the range of a set of data.

3 I can sort events according to the probability of them happening and place them in order of likelihood.

4 I can choose a fair method of selecting things at random and know when a method is unfair.

5 I can estimate the chance of an event happening, using a scale from 0% to 100%.

Number and algebra

1 I can understand instructions when they contain the words *if* and *then*.

2 I can use instructions that contain the words *and* and *not* in mathematical situations.

3 I can use rules with number sequences and relationships between number columns.

4 I understand how a computer spreadsheet is used, and can write a formula for a cell.

5 I can replace symbols in formulas (or rules) with different numbers to find the answer.

6 I can solve an equation by trial and improvement to find the value that gives the right result.

Shape and space

1 I can recognise different types of triangles by the sides and angles they have.

2 I can use a protractor or an angle maker to measure angles.

3 I can recognise a shape has been moved to a new position through combinations of horizontal and vertical movements.

4 I can recognise reflection in a grid, and being able to give co-ordinates of reflected points.

5 I can recognise rotational symmetry in 2D and 3D shapes.

Acknowledgements

Every effort has been made to contact the holders of copyright material, but if any have been inadvertently overlooked the publishers will be pleased to make the necessary arrangements at the first opportunity.

The publishers would like to thank the following for permission to reproduce photographs (T = Top, B = Bottom, C = Centre, L= Left, R = Right):

Allsport/C Brunskill, 6, G M Prior, 10, B Radford, 41;
J Morris/Axiom, 49;
Photos from www.JohnBirdsall.co.uk, 57, 122L;
Chris Bonington Photo Library/D Scott, 44;
(c) Carlton Television, 37;
John Ridley/ Crystal Maze: A Chatsworth Television Production for C4, 104;
Bruce Coleman/J Murray, 35;
(c) Crown. Reproduced by permission of the Controller of HMSO, 78;
Ronald Grant Archives, 51TL&BL, 68;
Sally & Richard Greenhill Photo Library, 30;
Kit Houghton Photo Library, 72
Andrew Lambert, 39, 100, 102, 113, 122R;
LEGOLAND Windsor Park Ltd, 54;
London Weekend Television Ltd, 91;
Panos Photo Library/F Hoogervorst, 70;
Popperfoto/Reuters, 76, 107;
Rex Features Ltd, 8, 46, 51C&CR, 89, 116, 122C;
Science Photo Library/G East, 85 (inset), R Scagelt, 85T;
Science Museum/Science & Society Picture Library, 110;
Tony Stone Images, 12, 23, 26, 28, 51CL&TR, 81, 119;
Telegraph Colour Library, 17, 20;
John Walmsley Photography, 94, 98.